MW00355225

THE
BLUE
HOLES
OF THE
BAHAMAS

THE
BLUE
HOLES
OF THE
BAHAMAS

ROBERT PALMER

JONATHAN CAPE
THIRTY-TWO BEDFORD SQUARE LONDON

For George Benjamin

First published 1985
Copyright © 1985 by Robert Palmer
Jonathan Cape Ltd, 32 Bedford Square, London WC1B 3EL

British Library Cataloguing in Publication Data

Palmer, Robert
The blue holes of the Bahamas.
1. Cave diving——Bahamas——History——20th century
I. Title
917.296'04   F1651

ISBN 0–224–02311–X

Phototypeset by Falcon Graphic Art Ltd, Wallington, Surrey
Printed in Great Britain by
R.J. Acford Ltd, Chichester, Sussex

Contents

Illustrations

The author and publishers would like to thank the following for permission to include photographs: George Benjamin Collection (no. 12), Sarah Cunliffe (no. 60), Leo Dickinson (no. 43), Mandy Dickinson (no. 70), Lucy Heath (nos 68, 69, 72-3, 75), Rob Parker (nos 33, 42, 44, 59, 61, 77), Peter Scoones (no. 58) and Dennis Williams (nos 21-3). All other photographs were taken by the author himself.

Maps

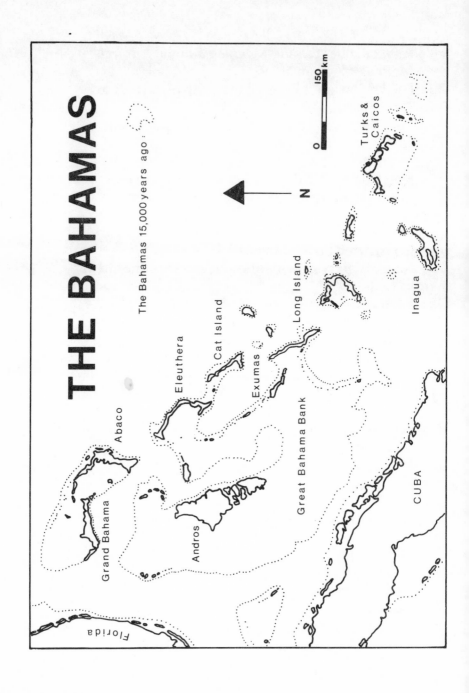

THE BAHAMAS

The Bahamas 15,000 years ago

N

150 km

Turks & Caicos

Inagua

CUBA

Long Island

Exumas

Cat Island

Eleuthera

Great Bahama Bank

Abaco

Andros

Grand Bahama

Florida

1

In the Beginning

Under the hot noon sun, three figures pulled a laden Zodiac inflatable through the shallows of Big Creek, zig-zagging through banks of broken finger-coral and haphazard legions of black, spiny sea-urchins, razor-sharp guardians of the bay. Across the sand-bars, exposed by a retreating tide, a raucous gang of pelicans strutted the wet beach. Beneath our feet, in the warm, clear waters, bright fish danced in the dappled sunshine. An abandoned, primeval air permeated the scene; we were the odd ones out, the intruders.

From above, on an aerial run along the coast of eastern Grand Bahama, the blue holes had been obvious. Now, level with the sea, they were more elusive. It took a few minutes to find the first one and establish the line. Then they seemed to be everywhere. The bay stretched south for almost two kilometres, and the chain of holes spanned its entire reach. A few metres from the sharp limestone shore, we stopped, as the water became too shallow for even the low draught of the Zodiac. Pulling it further inshore might mean a wait of several hours before the tide returned to float it out. Julian reached in, picked up the anchor, and buried it in the sands of the seafloor with his hands.

Eastern Grand Bahama from above had been a riot of colour. The wing-tips of our small plane had dipped over mangroves and bright sand, blue jigsaws of tidal creeks and land-locked lakes, tropical pine woodland and bare limestone rock, the bones of the island below. Here, at its eastern extreme, the long mainland gave up its struggle with the sea and fell to an invasion of ocean. The complex network of tidal creeks and shallow bays broke the area into a maze of small inlets and long sandy cays. Offshore, to the south, the sea took on a deeper hue as the fringing reef gave way to an ocean drop-off and the seafloor tumbled away into midnight, a thousand fathoms below.

The nose of the plane turned west along the southern coast. A long, sweeping bay appeared. Deep, underwater cave entrances flashed beneath us in a turquoise chain, standing out in marked contrast to the sandy blue shallows of the bay. In one kilometre-long stretch we could make out thirty openings, that ran in a straight line beside the shore. It was one of the most spectacular concentrations of blue holes we had ever seen.

The Zodiac floated next to the shore as we wandered like excited children in a secret garden. Sunshine glanced down rocky fissures into the enticing depths below, as we each chose a special place to explore.

We made ourselves ready at the boat, leaving one by one as we gathered up our gear. Air tanks were strapped to our sides, each with its own regulator in case one of the breathing sets were to fail deep inside a cave, where there would be no hope of surfacing. A plethora of equipment, all necessary for underground, underwater exploration, was checked with nervous anticipation before we slipped beneath the waters of the bay.

Julian chose a double cleft, a cool cave beside a broken stand of brain-coral, a little offset from the main line of holes. He was first to dive.

He disappeared with a casual O.K. sign. The entrance was narrow, filled with dozens of the sharp, black urchins that inhabited the bay, and which made their presence felt all too painfully with any careless stroke of a fin. Their long spines were sharp enough to penetrate even thick rubber flippers, but were also brittle enough to break off at the slightest lateral movement, leaving dark fragments buried deep beneath the skin. Julian nudged a clear path with his line reel, tumbling the unpleasant echinoderms into the void below.

For over thirty metres he edged down, forcing a way through a narrow sloping rift, half a metre at its widest, barely big enough to allow him through. Behind him, in the darkness, he left a thin nylon guideline that he unreeled as he swam, tying it to rocks jammed in the rift, to ensure that it led back through the widest sections of the narrow cave. A careless tug, or incautious tie, might drag it into a gap too narrow to pass on the return. If visibility were lost in clouds of rising silt – always a possibility in underwater caves – such a mistake could prove extremely dangerous.

Julian made his way slowly, in and down. Around him, the walls of the cave were alive with a rainbow assortment of tiny sponges, anemones, hydroids, the ubiquitous urchins, and bright, tiny shrimps. A host of multi-coloured fish, sheltering in the crevices of the cave, hid from the noisy intruder that broke in on their underground world. Crawfish scurried further into cracks. Fan-worms darted into their limestone tubes. Crabs fled.

Suddenly the cave changed. A last push in the dark and claustrophobic rift brought Julian tumbling out over the head of a black, underground void, deep under the rock of the bay, plunging even deeper into the darkness below, a seemingly bottomless pit. Such a sudden change was a little unnerving.

Unsure of what lay in wait in the darkness, Julian bled a little of the air from his buoyancy jacket and allowed himself to drift cautiously down. The cave grew bigger. One hundred metres in from the entrance, Julian looked at his depth gauge. Forty-two metres registered, enough for one dive. He cut the line on the reel, and tied the end to a rock flake that jutted out from one wall. With a last look at the still-descending cave, he turned and began to feel his way cautiously out.

Meanwhile, Rob Parker was entering a shaft in the centre of a small chain of blue holes a few metres from the shore. His eyes took a moment to adjust to the darkness, but then he stopped in sudden apprehension. The shaft was no narrow cleft, bounded closely by rock walls, but an immense underwater cavern, one of the largest underwater caves he had ever encountered. On all sides, the walls faded away into darkness, and he felt almost agoraphobic, glancing nervously from side to side, overwhelmed by a sense of being watched by something large, carnivorous and unfriendly.

Through five entrances that led in from above, shafts of sunlight spread a faint blue light throughout the cavern, slanting down eerily to the sandy floor below. On the sides of the hall, strangely shaped stalactites hung from the roof, mirrored below by rising columns of stalagmites. Rob hung suspended in the centre of this mystic underworld, in clear, dark water, taking in the scene. Then, tying his line to the entrance wall, he moved off to explore.

Above, I was alone on the surface. I moved through the shallows towards the great chasm in its centre, floundering through the water under the weight of the large twin air tanks on my side. I had chosen the largest opening, previously christened Manta Hole, a deep collapse in the centre of the chain, over sixty metres long and half that wide.

Earlier that year Dennis Williams, a Grand Bahama cave-diver, had visited the area briefly and explored a passage in this cave for about a hundred and fifty metres in the direction of a small lake that lay inland about a kilometre to the north. In the lake was a small blue hole, and I hoped for a connection between the two, making a long underwater traverse between lake and bay. Dennis and his companion had reached a massive boulder collapse at their furthest point, at a depth of thirty-three metres. Wearing bulky, back-mounted tanks, they were unable to find any way through. Our more streamlined side-slung tanks might enable us to negotiate a way past the blockage and explore the new cave beyond.

In the Beginning

There was much activity in the entrance to Manta Hole. Caught in the last of the daylight, a small green octopus and an angry Bahamian crawfish were physically deciding which would be lunch. The debate stumbled to a halt as they became aware of my presence, and they scurried off to their respective corners to await suitable conditions for round two.

Passing into the dark cave beyond, I followed the old, encrusted guideline into the passage. The opening of the cave was large, four metres high and over two wide, its rock walls lined with tenacious life, the floor an expanse of dunes formed from coarse sands carried in by the currents that scoured the cave for most of the day. At the precise moment when the reversing tidal currents slackened off before they changed direction, exploration could be made.

One hundred metres in, a junction appeared in the line: a thin cord ran upwards from the main line into the roof above. Dennis had mentioned that this led to a gallery of stalactites high in the roof of the cave. It also meant that I was getting close to the choke at the end.

A jumble of broken rocks loomed out of the darkness, casting peculiar shadows in the light of my torches. I paused and looked at my depth gauge. Thirty-three metres. I checked the air in my tanks, and then tied my own reel on to the end of the old line. As I prepared to explore, I grew aware that not all the movement in the rock pile was shadow. Moving sinuously through the boulders, only a few metres away, was the largest moray eel I had ever seen!

Of all the irrational fears experienced by the cave-diver, the possibility of meeting something large and unfriendly deep in a cave is one of the worst. It is one of those atavistic fears that are born of terror and inbred apprehension. Suddenly it did not seem so irrational any more.

I hung motionless for several moments, uncertain of what to do. My torches followed every movement of the eel. It watched me just as closely, its mean, tiny eyes glinting in the light. Huge jaws opened and shut in an hypnotic rhythm, showing three rows of hooked teeth that gleamed in the beam of the torch. I could vividly imagine a sudden dart and a fierce bite. With its tail anchored firmly in the rock pile, and its powerful jaws gripping me in an unbreakable vice, there would be little hope of escape before my air ran out.

If I tried to move past, what would it do? If I turned and fled away, what would it do, come to that? Was it hungry, living this far back in the cave? Was it as scared as I was, dazzled by the sudden light? That was hard to believe; my pulse rate was soaring! I could hear every heartbeat. Normally morays are shy creatures, retreating from contact with humans. How much rules might differ in this environment, I could not guess.

Slowly the fear turned to a peculiar irritation. The end of the cave was so near, just beyond this living barrier. I rose higher in the water and, looking down on the eel, moved slowly and cautiously past, leaving it to the enveloping darkness behind. I swam on with an itching feeling in my feet, praying it would not follow!

A few metres on, I met the blockage. Massive boulders were jammed across the cave in a seemingly impenetrable jumble of rock. Moving delicately up and over the pile, I looked for a way through at every level, at every angle. Slabs of rock were perched precariously on top of each other. As I pushed against one it shifted slightly. At the highest point of the choke a few stalactites leant drunkenly beneath the topmost rocks, mere centimetres from the roof. The blockage was complete. Not wishing to tempt fate a second time, I kept high in the passage until I was sure I had passed the giant eel below. Then, sinking down to rejoin the line, I headed out.

The warm sunlight at the entrance was a welcome sight. I had spent over half an hour at the depth of thirty-three metres; this meant a wait of several minutes at three metres, allowing the accumulated nitrogen to decompress from my body tissues, to avoid any chance of the 'bends', which can cripple a diver. On the south side of the large entrance, at precisely that depth, I came across a smaller passage that headed seawards, in the opposite direction to the first. I checked my air supply, and decided that I had just enough to spare for a brief exploration here. Tying the line to a coral-encrusted rock, I swam into the darkness again.

This time my sojourn underground was even more brief. Around the first bend was a five-foot nurse shark, wanting to go the other way. I gave up, wound the line back on to the reel, and headed out. Some days are easier than others.

Blue holes are the entrances to some of the world's most spectacular underwater caves. Native Bahamians call them blowing or boiling holes, in deference to the fierce tidal currents that pulse in and out of marine entrances in an only partially-predictable cycle, making these peculiar caves extremely dangerous to explore.

Caves form mainly in limestone, and Bahamian limestone is the thickest and most stable mass known anywhere in the world. From the tip of Cat Island, barely sixty metres above the sea and the highest point in the islands, to the deep foundations of the Bahama platform is five vertical miles of rock. These horizontal layers, or beds, of limestone represent over a hundred million years of slow sediment accumulation in shallow seas, a timescale almost too great to imagine. *Tyrannosaurus rex* had still to walk the earth when the Bahamas began to form.

In those days the continents, as we now know them, were part of a great primeval land mass called Panagea, which began to fragment as stresses within the surface of the Earth pulled it apart. On the eastern edge of the fragment that would eventually become North America, an area of coral reef and shallow sea began to form. Smaller, more localised stresses in the bedrock lifted parts of the region a little above the surrounding seafloor. New growth added weight to these shallower reefs and the whole area began very, very slowly to subside – just one centimetre every hundred years or so. As the area began to sink, the reefs continued to grow upwards towards the sun, layer on layer, the topmost corals always growing just below the surface of the sea. The deeper regions became channels between the reefs, scoured by ocean currents, and too deep for reef-building corals to grow. Today, over a thousand metres separate the ocean floor that surrounds the Bahama banks from the air above.

Exactly when caves began to form in the Bahamian limestone is not known. They may be relatively recent features, or they may have their beginnings many millions of years in the past, early in the geological history of the Bahamas. Early caves would now lie thousands of metres below the surface, full of mud, water and later re-crystallisation of minerals. Many may simply have collapsed under the pressure of the overlying rock. Several years ago on Andros, the largest of the Bahamian islands, a drilling company sank a borehole near Stafford Creek. At a depth of over 3,000 metres they encountered a natural cavity over ten metres high. Another similar cavity lay a few metres deeper. Here, the drill pipe buckled and over 2,400 metres of tubing was lost within the cave. A decent hole, by any standards!

The caves that interested us were more recent. These lie within the top few hundred metres of the limestone, and have been formed during the last million years by chemical activity at the base of the freshwater tables of the islands, where the rainwater floats on top of the denser saltwater beneath.

Most limestone islands like the Bahamas have this floating mass of freshwater, broken up by marine intrusions such as creeks or bays into a series of separate lens-shaped bodies. The freshwater itself may be the accumulation of many thousands of years of rainfall, stored in this natural underground reservoir. On Andros, the largest island, the base of a lens can be thirty metres beneath the level of the surrounding sea; on Grand Bahama, it is rarely deeper than fifteen to twenty metres.

The actual base of a lens, the interface between freshwater and saltwater, is called the halocline.

This is the level at which caves form. Variations in the chemical content of the water, coupled with a gentle tidal flow beneath the freshwater, make it possible for limestone to be dissolved more efficiently at the halocline. First of all, little enclosed solutional pockets form. These gradually become linked as the moving waters enlarge the natural cracks and joints in the rock. Slowly but surely, an open maze of passages is formed.

The story does not end there. At certain times in the last million years the global climate has undergone a marked change. Polar ice caps have expanded, to cover great areas of the world in a thick layer of glacial ice. The water that froze into the snows of the ice ages had to come from somewhere and most of it came from the oceans. At the greatest extent of the glaciers, the sea fell to over a hundred and twenty metres below present levels, and the Bahamas underwent radical change. From being a widespread, scattered group of island basking beneath a hot sun, the region became one of high limestone plateaux, edged by steep cliffs, standing a hundred metres and more above the waves.

The freshwater lenses fell with the sea, and expanded dramatically in extent below the new land mass. Where the seas paused in their vertical migration for long enough, caves continued to form. Fractures along the edge of the plateaux, and faults inland, allowed them to develop vertically as well as horizontally, linking the different levels of development and creating a three-dimensional maze beneath the Bahamas. Then, as the ice melted and the seas rose, this underworld was drowned. The waters of the ocean slowly flowed into older, higher caves, flooding beautiful grottos of stalagmites and stalactites which had formed in the dry air of the exposed caverns. Fish, anemones, sponges and bright, scurrying crustaceans of all shapes and sizes moved in to make these caves their home. Living and dying in utter blackness, far from the light of the open ocean, some began to adapt gradually to their peculiar underworld. They joined creatures that had started along this road millions of years before, moving upwards with the rising seas from ancient caves deeper in the Bahamian rocks.

Man moved into the Bahamas before the seas ceased rising, barely 5,000 years ago. He knew and used some of the higher caves, a few of which are still dry today. Some of his sites now lie a few metres underwater, though these would be largely obscured by newer sediments in the cave mouths. Only in one or two such places is there evidence of his passing. In the waters of the Lucayan Caverns on Grand Bahama is the communal grave mound of several Lucayan Indians, the earliest known inhabitants of the islands. The top of the mound may originally have extended out of the waters of the underground lake in which it lies, a cone of boulders reaching towards a single opening in the cave roof above. Today, the mound lies spectacularly underwater. When the sun is overhead, a single shaft of light pierces the darkness, lancing down through the clear water to illuminate the top of the mound. The individuals buried here must have been great indeed to warrant such a monument. Who they were, we shall never know. The Lucayan Indians and their gentle Arawak successors were shipped by the Spaniards to die in the gold and silver mines of Hispaniola, a careless act of genocide that brought to an abrupt end an Indian civilisation over two thousand years old.

One by one, we surfaced in Big Creek and gasped our discoveries to each other. Many entrances remained to be explored, but the tide was nearing low; if we stopped to talk we would be stranded. Stories could be swopped in more detail when diving gear was in the boat, and we were on the move again through the shallows, dragging the Zodiac behind.

Manta Hole had been named by its original American explorers, but we felt the others were deserving of a little

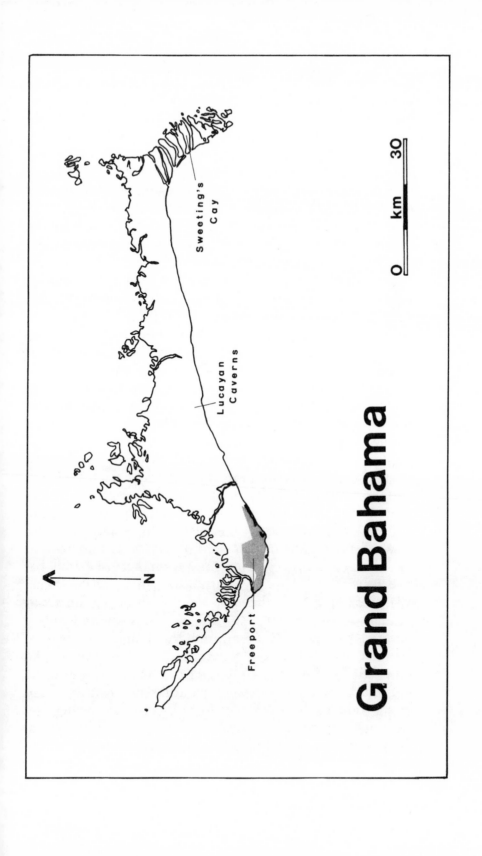

Grand Bahama

more romance. In a fit of Tolkienism, Julian's twin entrances became Helm's Deep; Rob Parker's charismatic, mysterious underwater hall would be known as Lothlorien, Tolkien's 'dreamflower'.

South of Big Creek, about two kilometres further along the coast, lies a remote and beautiful bay, Thrift Harbour. Few people ever go there, the long white beach is bare of footprints and the debris of humanity. Conch shells move in the shallows near the shore, and mud skippers shuffle on muscular fins from pool to pool in between young shoots of mangrove, green against the white sands.

A small blue hole at the entrance to the bay was hidden behind a mobile group of tiny silversides, small fry that swarmed as one in a myriad shoal in the cool outflowing water from the low entrance. In one fluid movement they seemed to absorb the arm I thrust into the middle of their insubstantial mass. Not one of the tiny fish touched it; they simply altered the pattern of their movement to accept the intrusion. The sun threw light from microscopic scales in a shimmering kaleidoscope. The hole itself remained invisible, camouflaged by life.

We rode the Zodiac into the shallows and pulled to the shore. In a creek behind the bay, beyond a thick tangle of mangrove and scrub, lay another of the blue holes briefly visited by Dennis the year before. We had seen it from above, a ring of blue on the edge of the sandy creek.

Wind breathed through the tall casurinas that fringed the shoreline, concealing a muddy mangrove patch between us and the line of thornbushes that hid the creek. We stepped across the soft mud that oozed into our sandals as we headed for the scrub. Rob and Julian decided to find a way around the tangle. In devious laziness, I tried to force a way through. At the expense of a little skin, and with a few scratches from the spines of an unfamiliar plant, I was soon standing amongst the mangrove roots in the creekside. Ahead, across the water and just a little upstream, the deeper blue of the hole beckoned. Flies buzzed around, butterflies skittered above the water, a lone turkey-buzzard circled silently overhead, playing in the warm thermals. In the distance, Rob and Julian could be heard still trying to find a way round. Time was on tickover, the scene had a lazy, indolent air. Holding my camera high, I waded out into the warm waters of the creek, churning brown mud in a cloud around my feet. It proved an inadvisable move.

Half-way out from the shore, I passed a thin grey shape beneath the rippled surface. A small shark, maybe a lemon, or a nurse, was dozing in the warm shallows. We had come across such basking beasts before but, as they tended to ignore us, we grew to ignore them. Never trust a shark!

This one must have woken up as I passed, and caught the movement in the corner of its eye. Movement meant food, it could have mistaken my ankle for a crab or a small fish. A grey streak flashed across the intervening space, heading straight for my legs.

Instinctively, I leapt almost clean out of the water. The shark passed beneath me. I landed, it turned, we repeated the process. Up I went again, hoping that it would miss, or that at least I might land on top of it and scare it off. It made a final pass and disappeared, possibly deciding there were easier meals elsewhere. I took bare seconds to reach the shore, hot, angry and frightened, with a ruined camera dripping with saltwater. Rob and Julian were near by, made anxious by my shouting, and hurrying to help. We were more careful about solo exploration in creeks after that. An accident so far from civilisation could easily prove fatal; it would be far from amusing to survive all the dangers of underwater cave exploration only to fall foul of something nasty on the surface.

On the long ride back to our base (the floor of the village school in MacLean's Town, on the Grand Bahama mainland), we passed another of the jumble of islets that make up the broken jigsaw of East End. Behind the fringing dunes and rocky bluffs of its shoreline, a flat expanse of tropical pine forest, thick thorn-scrub and rocky limestone barrens extended for several kilometres. On the north shore of this island, Sweeting's Cay, we located a narrow mangrove creek that branched into two channels. At the end of each branch lay a blue hole. These would be our next destination, and they would turn out to be the first pieces of a magnificent underground maze – the Zodiac Caverns of Grand Bahama.

2

The Blue Holes of Andros

I first encountered the term blue holes in a draughty hall in Sheffield. I was attending the annual British caving conference in 1976, having just begun my cave-diving career, making short penetrations in the cold, flooded passages of Yorkshire caves. At that time, British cave-diving was becoming increasingly sophisticated. Even so, there were very few divers who had swum more than two or three hundred metres down submerged caves, and then only at shallow depths. I was not one of them.

An expatriate British caver, Alf Latham, had brought to the conference a film made by George Benjamin, a Canadian cave-diver. Benjamin, Latvian by birth, was quite a character, with a strong accent and completely shaven head. He had been exploring extensive underwater cave-systems off the Bahamian island of Andros, using techniques far in advance of those used in Britain, and making explorations of over 500 metres into caves, at depths in excess of fifty metres. The caves were breathtaking, but the thought of such isolation, and such obviously difficult technical diving, sent a chill through me. I put blue holes well down on my list of places to visit, and continued to develop my own primitive skills under the Yorkshire Dales.

In Britain, the sport has developed through the exploration of cold, dark tunnels, virtually devoid of life, where the rivers of upland limestone hills carve their underground course down towards the sea. Most of the underwater sections of these caves are part-filled with fine mud, or peaty sediments, and visibility underwater is rarely more than a metre or two, and often much less. The clarity of an inward swim is usually in marked contrast to that of the exit, when the fine sediments have been disturbed from floor and walls to hang in suspension in mid-water in the wake of the diver's passage. It is often impossible in these circumstances to see a hand held closely in front of a facemask, and touch alone must provide a sensory awareness of the cave around. The temperature rarely exceeds 7 or 8 degrees centigrade, and the creeping, numbing cold adds to the inherent dangers of the environment itself, reducing the diver's ability to react instantly and efficiently to crises and making physical dexterity a joke.

To reach many of the sumps (as flooded passages are called) in British caves often involves hours of struggle through dry passages that are themselves difficult and demanding to negotiate. Carrying metal air tanks, pumped to over 200 times the surrounding air pressure, along awkward rocky tunnels, or hauling them down deep vertical shafts, is an unnerving business. Each clang, each metallic ring, is greeted with a wince. Cavers tread more warily when carrying such gear. Even greater care is taken with the box carrying the regulators, the machinery that keeps the diver alive by reducing the tremendously high air pressure in the tanks to that of the surrounding environment and delivering air as the diver's lungs demand. Even amongst ordinary cavers, cave-*divers* are regarded as extremists, dedicated fools who work at the very limits of endurance.

Cave-diving began beneath the Mendip Hills of Somerset, in 1935. Two caves several miles apart were discovered to have a hydrological link when dye poured into one emerged from the other on the next day. The stream that sank into the first of these caves, Swildon's Hole, followed a steeply descending course through dark rock tunnels and down narrow passages for several thousand metres deep below the Mendip fields. At length it disappeared into a seemingly impenetrable pool and was next seen in the well-known show cave of Wookey Hole, in the Mendip foothills. The River Axe, as it had now become, was a greater stream than that in Swildon's Hole alone. The long and unexplored passages which lay between must contain many kilometres of passages and tributary tunnels. The possibility of entering these and walking down caverns that had never seen the passage of man was a tantalising challenge. A small group of expert cavers, led by Graham Balcombe, obtained bulky commercial diving equipment, complete with the classic brass divers' helmets, and began the upstream exploration of Wookey Hole. Lumbering along the bottom of the underwater cave, in clumsy lead boots and trailing behind them a thick, heavy umbilical cord of air and communication hoses, these early, brave explorers were the forerunners of the solo, free-swimming cave-divers of today.

The intervening fifty years saw a haphazard progress in the sport. It was not until the 1950s that fins came into common use, replacing the clumsy bottom-walking technique, oxygen rebreathers having replaced the traditional umbilical suit in the immediate post-war years. Despite the growing popularity of the air-filled aqualung, which enabled divers to stay down longer and dive deeper than on oxygen, it was not until the 1960s that it was adopted by cave-divers. Freed from the encumbrance of rebreathers, a golden age of British cave-diving followed.

By 1970, exploration of Swildon's Hole had been extended to an impenetrable squeeze in the twelfth sump, and in Wookey Hole divers had progressed from Chamber Three, the original diving base, to Chamber Twenty-Two, negotiating over 400 metres of flooded passages in between. By then, the long caves of Ogof Fynnon Ddu in Wales, and Langstroth and Kingsdale in Yorkshire, had been discovered, largely by divers. During that decade, a

2,000 metre underwater connection was forged between the Kingsdale Master Cave and Keld Head risings, heralding a new era in cave-diving in Britain – the exploration of a long, flooded cave-system for its own sake. No longer were diving techniques used simply to pass flooded barriers in the hope of reaching new air-filled caves. New techniques developed to cope with long-distance underwater caving on the Keld Head dives meant that caves such as the blue holes, despite their obviously greater depths, were now more practically within reach of British cave-divers!

George Benjamin was a man ahead of his time in the cave-diving world. In the late 1960s, he became fascinated by the enigmatic underwater openings in the seafloor around Andros Island. With a small group of friends, all expert divers, he began a systematic cataloguing of the marine caves off the eastern shore of the island. The larger and more interesting caves they began to explore.

Even in the late 1960s, equipment was far from sophisticated. In common with cave-divers everywhere, Benjamin had to develop much of his own equipment in order to explore the caves with an acceptable degree of safety. His experience of underwater photography helped him. His team-members designed powerful lighting units which allowed longer penetrations to be made in caves that soaked up the beams of the puny diving torches available at the time. Recognising the possibility of breathing equipment failing deep within one of the caves, they developed a common manifold to link twin back-mounted tanks together. Two regulators were attached to this manifold, and if one failed, a quick turn of a tap would isolate it from the rest of the breathing system, thus minimising air loss. The other regulator maintained access through a manifold to all the air in both tanks. Up to then, with a separate regulator on each tank, a valve failure would leave the divers with a tank full of air that he could not use.

The Benjamin Crossover manifold was not only a

practical advance in cave-diving equipment but also provided a psychological boost for the explorers. The further one swims from airspace, the greater the dependence on suitable equipment becomes.

Benjamin explored many blue holes with this refined gear, but became increasingly drawn to one system in the South Bight of Andros. The Bight is a long marine creek, that splits the island from east to west. There are a number of blue holes in the creek, and the currents that pulse in and out of their entrances made it obvious that a great cave-system existed beneath. Led by George Benjamin and Peter, his son, divers began a systematic exploration of the South Bight caves.

They discovered ten entrances in all, revealing caves that ranged from tiny water outlets to huge openings ten metres across. There was one cave, however, that proved to be more exciting than all the others, the fourth of a line of holes that ran from north to south across the mouth of the creek. Now called Benjamin's Blue Hole, it still ranks as one of the world's greatest underwater caves, nearly twenty years after its first exploration.

Benjamin made his first descent at Christmas 1967, waiting until the fierce current slackened off enough to allow a safe entry. The way in lay down a narrow cleft, dropping vertically into the rock floor of the Bight. Twenty metres down, they could still just see daylight above, but the cave soon narrowed into a constricted gap. Passing through this, they discovered a cavern larger than anything they had so far encountered. It took several attempts to reach the bottom of the shaft, fifty metres down, but Peter Benjamin was the first there, soon followed by the rest of the team. They carried shark guns, in case they came across the monsters the natives swore lurked in the caves, but met nothing. The narrow entrance and strong currents were enough to keep the more frightening denizens of the open sea out of the cave.

Their early explorations took them only fifty metres from the bottom of the pit. Peter paid out coils of thick nylon to guide their path back, and reached the edge of a large chamber as the line ran out. The cave disappeared on beyond the range of his spotlight, but he could see the floor sloping down immediately in front of him to a depth of over sixty metres. It was to be several years before they could penetrate much further.

By the summer of 1970, Frank Martz had designed new lighting units in which the bulky battery-pack could be separated from the torch, and worn on the waist. The thirty-watt torch was linked to this by a flexible wire, and a five-watt back-up bulb in the torch gave a spare light in case the main bulb failed. Hand-held coils of thick nylon safety-rope were replaced by compact reels of strong nylon cord, thinner and much easier to handle in the confined caves, the Crossover manifold had been developed, so explorations could now progress with a much greater degree of security than before.

To penetrate further, George Benjamin had to change the timing of his team's dives. The greatest clarity of the cave waters comes at the end of the outflow, when the particles that have been drawn in on the suction cycle have either settled or been blown back outside.

The visibility at this time can be breathtaking. By contrast, the inflow is murky, the waters carrying in all sorts of organic and inorganic debris from the surrounding seabed, material that feeds the life in the caves, but which does not aid clear vision! Then, a diver can see only a few metres at best. The original dives had been made during the brief pause at the end of the outflow, before the inflow began. Now they planned their dives for the other side of the cycle, to coincide with the slack water when the inflow stopped and the water was at its murkiest.

George and his team sacrificed clarity for a good reason. The currents in the blue hole were extremely strong, and if much time were spent exploring at the end of the outflow, divers risked being trapped inside the cave by the mounting suction. The inflow was so strong that it quickly created a whirlpool at the entrance. After studying the tides, a formula was developed which allowed them to predict the time of the changeover with reasonable accuracy – the tides do not, unfortunately, change in the caves at the same time they do in the sea, but over two hours later. If George and his divers timed their explorations well, they could expect some help from the growing outflow at the end of the slack, easing their swim out of the cave.

One of their first deep penetrations, in August 1970, was in a passage heading north, with little current and a very muddy floor. Sixty metres from the base of the entrance shaft, the passage widened, becoming over thirty metres high. Further dives took them through several large halls to a point 300 metres from the entrance, but they discovered no end to the tunnel.

George Benjamin's dream was to discover speleothems – stalagmites and stalactites – that could have grown only if the caves had once been dry. He was convinced that these caves had formed, as most limestone caves do, by the action of rivers flowing beneath the islands. During the time of lower sea-levels in the ice ages, when the Bahama plateaux were exposed, such rivers might have carved tunnels for themselves in the rock, carrying rainwater down to the new levels of the sea. In this he was not entirely right, but his explorations took him into blue holes along the length of Andros, looking for the crystal evidence that would prove that the caves had once lain above the level of the sea.

The depth of the Big Room reached by Peter Benjamin in the south passage of the South Bight cave had been the main barrier to further exploration. In 1970, divers discovered a small opening in the roof a few metres before the Big Room, and this was to prove the key to the vast South System beyond. In the new passage there were pillars of rock that looked suspiciously like speleothems but which were covered by centuries of marine overgrowth, riddled with the tunnels of boring tube-worms and molluscs. Were solid crystal columns to be found beneath the encrustation, formed when stalagmite and stalactite had met? Or were they all simply peculiar shapes in the rock, the result of an unusual quirk of geology? The search for more positive proof went on.

Behind the pillars, the passage narrowed. The divers swam at a depth of forty-five metres and could feel a slight current pushing against them. After 120 metres they emerged in an enormous hall. They could only guess at its size as the beams of their lights were swallowed up in the immensity of the cavern. Huge blocks littered the floor, and one giant slab was wedged across the cave, a meaningless natural bridge, deep underwater. There their line ran out: they were almost 250 metres from the entrance and forty-five metres down.

George's own words take up the story.

The clarity was good, our air supply adequate, and the conditions ideal for taking pictures. I was holding on to the lifeline (it happened to be the end), Dick Williams went fifty feet ahead using the firing cord from my camera to his strobe as an additional lifeline. Tom Mount was a short distance ahead, not more than twenty to thirty feet, as no one should venture far away without a line. This set-up was our standard procedure for taking pictures, and the diver in front of the strobe served mainly to introduce a scale into the picture.

Within the reach of Tom's searchlight, there was a faint outline of a cavern full of stalagmites and stalactites, not only the few we had seen before, but hundreds of them. I switched off my lights to view the scene from total darkness. It was like the front centre seat for the greatest show on earth! I triggered the strobe. The brilliant flash momentarily lit up the whole cave. It was only the beginning, there were many more formations further in. Minutes passed like seconds. It is a hidden danger that during excitement like this we forget to watch our air supply gauges. We turned back. Swimming was easy as the current was with us. During

1 Entering a blue hole

2 The coast of Grand Bahama, a maze of tidal creeks

3 Divers kit up at an inland blue hole at Andros Island

4 Julian Walker peers into a blue hole in Big Creek

5 Looking into a blue hole, Grand Bahama

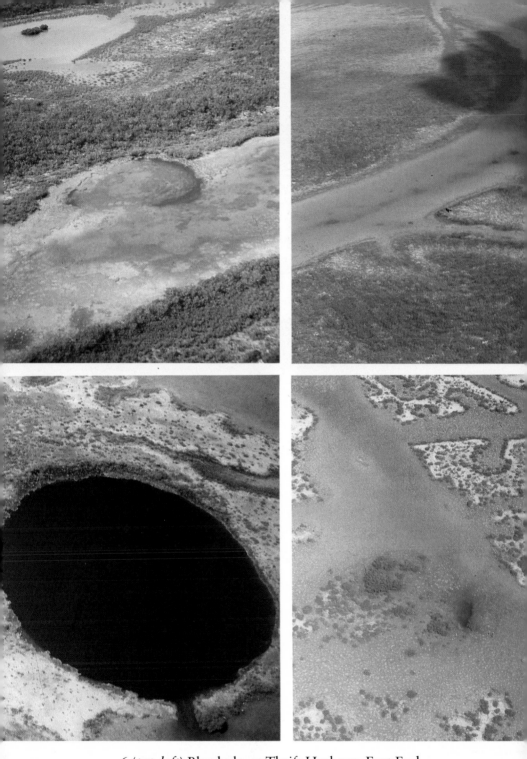

6 (*top left*) Blue hole, at Thrift Harbour, East End
7 (*top right*) Blue holes in a tidal creek, Grand Bahama
8 (*above left*) The 'Black Hole', Grand Bahama, an inland hole over sixty metres deep
9 (*above right*) A blue hole in a jigsaw of mud and mangroves

decompression, we communicated by writing messages on plastic boards to ask was it real or a dream, or hallucinations caused by nitrogen narcosis? Every one of us saw the stalagmites.

We realised this was the find we and other explorers had been looking for. We found the proper name for this undersea wonder by naming it simply 'The Grotto'. We do not expect this Grotto to become a mass tourist attraction like the Capri Blue Grotto. It is only for expert cave-divers, for those who can master the dangerous dive and are willing to undertake the almost half-mile swim to the Grotto and, most important, to preserve enough strength for getting out.

As luck would have it, the dive that revealed the stalagmites and stalactites was the last of that expedition. Everything was ready for departure the following morning and they had no chance to return for some time.

The French explorer and film-maker Jacques Cousteau came to Andros that summer to make a film on blue holes. George had spent some time with Cousteau and the crew of the *Calypso*, advising them on sites in which their efforts might be best rewarded. The discovery of the Grotto would make a marvellous climax to Cousteau's film, and George lost no time in contacting the Cousteau organisation. Eventually he persuaded them to return.

At Christmas, George and Peter laid thick nylon guidelines through to the Grotto. In a complex operation, not without its moments of drama for the less cave-experienced *Calypso* divers, the speleothem caverns of Benjamin's Blue Hole were caught on film to be shared with the rest of the world.

The great blue hole of South Bight was further explored in the next few months. George, Peter and Frank pressed on beyond the Grotto for 200 metres and came to a large pit in the floor of the cave, into which they sank until they reached a depth of eighty metres. Beneath them, the cave disappeared into unfathomable blackness, seeming to plunge into the very bowels of the island. Later on, divers Tom Mount and Ike Ikehara of Miami reached a point 600 metres from the entrance, passing over the top of the pit, at a depth of thirty metres. Side passages were discovered that revealed a new complexity to the cave. The divers were becoming ambitious, pushing new extremes, not only in the caves but in themselves, stretching technique to the limit. Though there were still horizontal passages to explore at shallower depths, the great lure was the deep pit beyond the Grotto, 400 metres into the cave. Ever since he had descended the great pit earlier that year, Frank had thought of returning and descending further into the mysterious shaft. No one knew what lay at the bottom. Whether it just pinched out, or whether it led to new and even more magnificent galleries, was a complete mystery.

In early September 1971, Frank Martz and Jim Lockwood entered the cave, reached the shaft and began their descent. Frank, the more experienced of the two, was wearing new equipment with which he had not completely familiarised himself. His knife, which he normally wore on his forearm, he had moved to his leg. After reaching the previous limit of exploration eighty metres down, they continued their descent until at eighty-five metres they reached a narrow constriction too small to pass easily with the bulky twin 100 cubic-foot tanks they wore on their backs. They were now deeper than either man had been before in an underwater cave.

Motioning Jim to wait, Frank approached the constriction and, moving very carefully, managed somehow to squeeze through, disappearing from Jim's sight. Jim waited for several minutes, growing increasingly concerned. They had very little air to spare at this depth. Despite the time, Frank did not reappear. Deeply worried, Jim ignored Frank's instruction and passed the constriction himself. All he found was a cut guideline, at a depth of almost 100 metres. Frank was dead, his body lost somewhere in the still-descending cave.

Why had he died? For a start, he had broken rules. He had dived deep, far deeper than before, with strange equipment. At depths of over thirty metres, the human mind is subject to the narcotic effect of the nitrogen in the air breathed and the effect is different with different people. Like alcohol, nitrogen narcosis heightens moods: some become lax, happy, overconfident; others are tense, nervous, afraid. Though experience of deep diving gives some ability to withstand the effect, no one is immune. At sixty metres, the threshold between control and panic is a narrow one. If an emergency occurs, it is easily crossed. At 100 metres, it barely exists at all. Frank had not been entirely well before the dive and his defences would have been low. He had been overconfident; had he become entangled in the line beyond the constriction, the stress might have been enough to push him over the panic edge. Like a man too drunk to stand, Frank had given himself too small a chance to pull through. Benjamin's Blue Hole claimed its victim.

Within three months, another of the regular team was dead. Archie Forfar, one of Benjamin's earliest blue hole diving companions, was another casualty of the lure of depth. Archie had become so enamoured of Andros that he set up his own diving resort at Stafford Creek, in the north of the island. From there some of the most spectacular diving outside the holes took place over the 'Wall', the immense 1,000 metre high underwater cliff that fringed the eastern shore of the island. Over this, the shallow reefs dropped away to the ocean floor far below in an instant, awe-inspiring plunge.

Archie was an expert diver and instructor, greatly experienced in deep diving. At that time there was a certain rivalry in Andros diving circles over who could go deepest. In sober reality there was little point to this. The variations in physiology that induce oxygen poisoning in any individual are still uncertain. Then, they were virtually unknown. When an individual dives extremely deep (disregarding for a moment the problem of narcosis that may have killed Martz), there comes a point at which the very level of oxygen in the air one breathes becomes toxic. The effects are instant and extreme. The diver convulses and loses consciousness. The only hope of survival lies in instant ascent. Diving very deep is like Russian roulette. You know you will survive only if you do.

Archie and his girlfriend were determined to set a world record for diving on ordinary compressed air in the deep ocean over the Wall. With a team of cover-divers and a support boat, they made their attempt on 11 December, 1971. Like Frank Martz, they were never seen again.

The first wave of blue hole exploration petered out shortly after that, although divers continued to enter the caves sporadically over the next decade.

Elsewhere in the world, the sport of cave-diving was flourishing, often in conditions that left British cave-divers a little envious! For years, they had been developing skills purely to extend dry caves, simply to seek air-filled passages. Outside Britain, cave-diving in water-filled caves was becoming an art in itself.

In 1979, in the French Grotte de la Bourne, Bernard Leger dived alone for over 1,000 metres. In Florida, not far from the Bahamas, Sheck Exley and Dale Sweet swam 1,380 metres into a spring with the original name of the 'Hole in the Wall', at a maximum depth of twenty-seven metres. And in Cocklebiddy Cave, beneath the arid Nullarbor Plain of Australia, cave-divers Hugh Morrison and Keith Dekkers, at a much shallower ten to fifteen metres, reached a point in the second of two long flooded passages 3,090 metres from the cave entrance, and over 2,000 metres from the short airspace that separated the two sumps. All this was underwater caving for its own sake, the state of the art in the late 1970s.

It appeared that British cave-diving was similar to British rock-climbing but the problems were often harder, more difficult and demanding in physical effort although, underwater, they were encountered in short bursts. The difficulties experienced in Britain, in cold, murky and often constricted sumps, gave experience and confidence in conditions that would be regarded as exceptionally severe elsewhere. But no one had any real experience of depth-diving, or of the decompression encountered after long duration underwater explorations.

The lure of large open passages, warm clear water, and caves that *lived*, in contrast to the dark and virtually lifeless British sumps, brought George Benjamin's film to mind. In 1979 I wrote to George, and received in return his complete catalogue of caves and explorations. He was, he felt, getting too old to continue with his own explorations, but was keen to see them carried on by others. In 1981, a small British team, which I led, arrived on Andros to see what we could do.

By chance, the base we found proved to be Archie Forfar's old diving resort, now run by International Field Studies of Ohio as a study centre. Treating things cautiously, we had chosen the northern end of Andros where it looked as though the caves were shallower than those further south. Despite this, we knew that we would be working in caves that were deeper and longer than any we had explored before.

I had gone out a few days ahead of the rest of the expedition and, while I waited, took the opportunity of making a few dives in some of the inland blue holes we would be exploring later. One of these had the peculiar name of Uncle Charlie's Blue Hole, named presumably after someone's long-dead Uncle Charlie who had once gone for a splash there. The Forfar Field Centre people used this as a swimming hole and Ken and Laurie Jones, our Centre guides, said that they had heard rumours of cave passages there.

In the middle of the lake we discovered a pit in the floor. The water in it was soupy and organic, with a strong sulphurous taste to it, and we almost went no further. It was horrible stuff to dive through, and I sank down feet-first past banks of organic gunge on all sides that looked as though any sudden movement would bring them tumbling in on top of me. I reached out to touch one of the walls and my arm disappeared up to the elbow without any feel of solidity to the loose mass. Just as I was about to give up, I came out into clear water, to see rock walls all around, and the cave continuing to drop away below me further than my torches' reach. Without their light, the cave would be black as the thick orange waters above cut out all daylight. Ken was above the sulphur layer, holding fast to one end of the line on my reel, primed to stay exactly where he was. Thrilled by my discovery, I continued down the shaft until the still-descending pit was bisected by a horizontal passage. One side disappeared in a tube a metre in diameter for as far as I could see. The other went a few metres and immediately turned a corner. For some reason the mysterious corner intrigued me more.

I swam in, turned the corner, and emerged in a small chamber. A glint in the roof caught my eye. I looked up and saw a diving torch hanging down from a cord. Slow on the uptake, I wondered how Ken could have found another way round. Then I realised what hung in the roof above the torch. I hadn't been first in the cave. Above me, the tattered, decaying remains of a previous explorer hung, wedged in the roof.

In the close silence of the small chamber, my immediate reaction was one of sorrow; no horror, no shrinking from the gruesome sight above. Here was someone like myself, who had pushed himself in the same way I had. A quick look at the remains showed that he had been ill-prepared. There was no sign of a guideline, and only a single torch and air tank. There were several possibilities, but the most obvious was that he had discovered the cave and had been fooled by the clarity of the water into exploring it without a line. Perhaps his torch went out or his regulator failed, but more probably he had simply swum into the small chamber and been unable to find the cave exit. A glance behind me told me why. The fine brown silt on the walls, the roof and the floor rolled around in thick brown clouds, stirred by the wake of my passing. The way out was invisible. As I hung there without moving, a fine cloud of particles drifted down from above, disturbed by my rising air-bubbles. I clung to the reel, my only link to the surface world. I could vividly imagine the horror felt by the corpse with which I shared the water – the brown clouds must have rolled into the chamber in the same way for him, but without a line to guide him out he had groped blindly around the rock walls in a desperate attempt to find the way back up the shaft by touch alone. After finding an upward crack, he must have tried to force his way up it, towards the surface. Then his air had run out.

It was one of the saddest moments of my cave-diving career, and as blunt a reminder as one could have at the start of a major expedition of the dangers of this environment. American cave-divers are told in their training manual that *'anyone* can die at *any* time on *any* cave-dive'. The unknown diver in Uncle Charlie's Blue Hole was less than thirty metres from safety. If he had taken a line, he could have exited on a single breath.

On the way back from the dive, we collected the rest of the team from the airport at San Andros. The grim announcement took the edge off the excitement of arrival and hammered home the seriousness of our intended work.

With me in the diving team were Martyn Farr and Rod Beaumont, both experienced divers, and George Warner, a marine biologist who had come to study the life in the ocean caves. Mel Gascoyne and Simcha Stroes were geologist and hydrologist, and Martyn and Rod had also brought their wives along. There was a slight holiday atmosphere; despite the serious side of our project we were not quite sure how seriously to take ourselves.

Our first few dives convinced us that we really had little to worry about. Our British training had given us a good start here. Clear warm water was a delight, and we soon discovered for ourselves what new rules there were.

Such currents were new to us. We watched, in stunned

amazement, the whirlpool at the entrance to Rat Cay Blue Hole, just north of the Field Station. George Benjamin had certainly not exaggerated the strength of the flow. We tried one day, in the same cave, to enter against the full force of the outflow. It was virtually impossible. We had to jam ourselves physically across the passage, rock-climbing horizontally in full diving gear, a ridiculous way to dive. Like Benjamin before us, we chose to concentrate on the brief time between the inflow and outflow, on the principle that we would rather be blown out than sucked in if we mistimed.

So we thought. On the first serious penetration we made in a cave on the far northern end of the island, beneath Conch Sound, Martyn and I dived in the last pull of the inflow, sure that the current was calming down to a stop. We laid out 200 metres of line in this dive, down a railway tunnel of a passage, up over a boulder pile, and straight out into an enormous hall full of stalagmites. We had found what George Benjamin had been searching for for years. And in a cave he himself had explored! His team had stopped only a few dozen metres short of the big chamber, still in the current-worn oval of the entrance tunnel. Full of excitement, we turned to swim back out of the cave. To our horror, we found that the current was still flowing in – and strongly!

We literally clambered hand-over-hand back down the passage, hauling ourselves bodily along 200 metres of cave. It was a closer thing than we wanted; after that we took rather more care.

It appeared the currents in Conch Sound could vary by as much as forty minutes either side of our average predicted time. It was by no means clear why the currents were there at all, or indeed why the tides in the caves reversed about three hours after the tides in the sea. George Benjamin had given some thought to this, and had decided that there must be a link between the deep oceanic trough that lay over the 'Wall', into which the edge of the island plunged. He thought that the cool outflow was water rising from the depths of the ocean through some curious thermal process. We wondered whether the inflow acted to lift the island's freshwater lens, flowing inland under the pressure from the tides at sea. The outflow would be the reverse – the pressure from the raised freshwater flushed the excess back along the same path, a hydrostatic head that forced the water to boil out of blue holes in a cool upwelling mound. Heat lost to the enclosing rock would account for the temperature difference between inflow and outflow.

There was another factor to consider. The tides on the western side of Andros had to flow across the wide, shallow Great Bahama Bank, eighty kilometres and more from where the Gulf Stream runs along the deep Florida Straits. By the time the tides reach the west coast of Andros, they lag several hours behind those on the east coast. This means that as currents are flowing into eastern blue holes, they are flowing out of those on the western side. When the eastern holes are blowing, the reverse happens. The main cause of the peculiar changeover time in the caves is due simply to tidal differences on either side of the island. Wind and weather are the culprits in the daily fluctuation. As they affect the precise timing of the surface tides, so do they affect the caves. Once we had realised this, we began to get a little better in our predictions.

Paradoxically, as we explored deeper into the caves, it mattered rather less. Deep inside, the currents were less strong, perhaps diffused into larger and diverging tunnels. As long as we could be sure that the changeover happened while we were inside the caves we felt safer, although unusually committed. Once in, struggling out against the current in an emergency was something none of us wanted to experience.

The tides changed swiftly in Conch Sound. The slack period lasted only momentarily before the current began to reverse. As we explored deeper into the cave, on dives lasting an hour and more, our exits became more sensational. We would be virtually shot down the tunnel towards the entrance by the force of the current, to end up drained at the foot of the wide and boulder-strewn amphitheatre after the most exhilarating of rides!

Conch Sound was proving the major discovery of the expedition. We traversed the first chamber to find another, swimming past brown, encrusted stalagmites that had seen the passing of an age underwater. They showed no sign of their crystal origin, save where some recent catastrophe had broken a pillar from its place of formation. Then the outer corroded layer could be seen to penetrate for less than a centimetre, and below that lay the clean, crystal core of pure calcite.

Beyond the stalagmite halls lay a desert. Here the sands which had been swept in on the tides of time had settled out. For over 200 metres Martyn and I swam across a wide expanse of dunes, a strange drowned landscape, over which tiny snake eels flew, and small crustaceans scurried, leaving irregular trails across the floor. Every now and again a small stalagmite grotto reared in fairy-tale towers from the sand, a welcome island to which to tie our guideline.

Just over half a kilometre from the entrance, the cave forked. On our last dive together that year, Martyn and I tied the line to the wall of the left-hand branch, at a depth of almost thirty metres. Then, while I was in Nassau playing politics with the customs over the expedition freight, Martyn made a solo dive down the other branch at the fork. This proved to be the main way on and, using five tanks of air, two as hand-held staging units to get him the first 300 metres, the other three worn on back and sides to press beyond, he reached a point where the roof had collapsed, 700 metres in. With little air to spare, he had no time to try to find a way through the pile of rocks. By the time he regained the entrance, he had worked up a decompression time as long as the dive itself. Our experience was expanding fast.

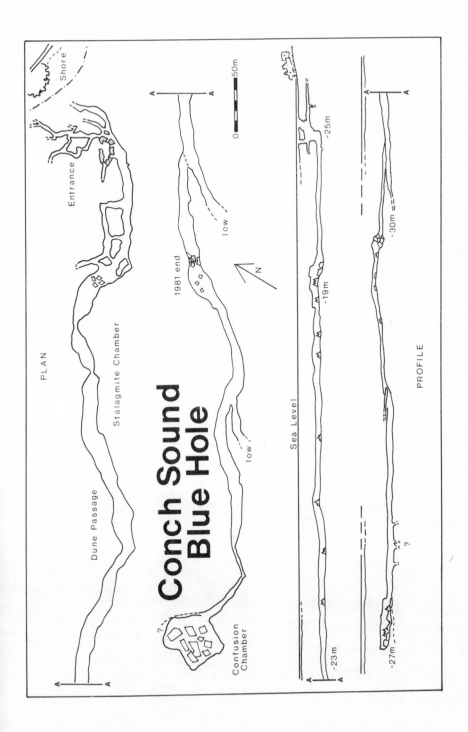

Conch Sound Blue Hole

PLAN

Shore

Entrance

Dune Passage

Stalagmite Chamber

Confusion Chamber

1981 end

low

low

N

0   50m

PROFILE

Sea Level

-19m

-23m

-25m

-27m

-30m

In 1982, Martyn and I returned with a larger team and more ambitious aims. We were sure that Conch Sound Blue Hole went further, and were intent on advancing beyond our previous limit to penetrate deeper into a submarine cave than anyone had ever done before. An expedition of fourteen had been difficult and more expensive to organise, and only the last minute addition of a film-crew had enabled us to go. The financial input from the film had been an absolute necessity, yet it caused strife. Martyn was not keen on the idea, or on my insistence on a scientific side to the venture. By the end of the first week there were sullen undercurrents in the team and tempers flared.

Fortunately the disagreements did not extend underwater. There, the teamwork was extraordinary, placing first Martyn and myself together beyond the boulder collapse, passing through a narrow gap between the rocks, and then each of us alone in turn in longer and longer dives, pushing the limits of the cave back at each attempt, and passing the kilometre mark.

Martyn's final push, taking him past my own 1,050 metre limit, took four divers working in close support, ferrying extra tanks into the cave for him to use as stage units, providing enough air for him to get to the end of the cave and beyond. Alone, and over 1,000 metres in, he reached a wide underwater chamber where he swam almost in a full circle before realising he could find no way on at a depth shallow enough to attempt. The flow seemed to come from deep crevices in the floor, just before the chamber. The formations at the far end of the cave, 1,150 metres from the entrance, were as pure as the days when they were formed, far from the destructive influence of the marine life near the entrance. Apart from two fragile ascidians, sea-squirts, the only sign of life was a solitary blind cave-fish, hanging silently in the still waters of the dark chamber. At the end of his line, Martyn was further into a submarine cave than anyone had previously explored.

By the end of the expedition, though, the division between us was deep and beyond easy healing. We had both behaved foolishly at times, a trust had been broken and, for whatever reasons, it would be difficult to work closely again. Martyn's drive meant he wanted to be out ahead. His main interests had been in where the cave went, and in being in front at the end. Although I had enjoyed my chance to be in front and had undoubtedly felt a great sense of achievement in reaching the kilometre point, I felt I was only half-exploring the cave. Increasingly, I wanted to know how and why the caves were there, and how life managed to exist in the deep recesses, so far from the outside world of sea and sun. What adaptions were necessary? How far in could life survive? The caves as a complete environment were the new lure – not just the physical exploration of their tunnels alone.

Before returning home, we spent a few days with Dennis Williams on Grand Bahama, who showed us the Lucayan Caverns. I realised there were other types of blue hole than those we knew from Andros. Long talks with Dennis fanned my interest in the caves themselves. Despite being thoroughly sick of the headaches of expedition planning, I decided that I would like to come back to Grand Bahama with a smaller team to look at the eastern end of the island. I had discovered I was not a great leader of men – a selfish wish to be closely involved with the various aspects of exploration gets too much in the way. I wanted to get to play too, and I hoped that with a group of three or four people, working closely together, it would be possible to avoid the social and organisational problems of the last expedition.

3

The Caves of Sweeting's Cay

Exploration is not a simple concept. It is a complex, many tiered ideal and it has as many branches as people have dreams. It encompasses all the exhilaration of being first, of being where no one has been before. It can embrace many forms, and can be experienced in geographical discovery, in philosophical or scientific study, in art or astronomy, or in more personal, spiritual terms.

For me, exploring underwater caves included more than mere curiosity of where the passage went. In the distant bounds of a cave, in the organisation of an expedition with all its attendant problems, I was exploring myself just as much as the caves I was using as a medium. Not that I always liked what I found. From the original, arrogant and emotional challenge of distance and depth, of setting transient human records, grew a softer and more natural curiosity. The old drives were still there but I wanted to explore more fully, and examine this new landscape on all its levels. In a way, the caves themselves had taken over; here was an underworld of colour, full of life, about which I had innumerable questions and too few answers.

In 1982, at the end of the Andros expedition, Dennis Williams flew us over the remote East End of Grand Bahama, over scores of unexplored blue entrances, at sea and inland. It was enough to kindle the embers of enthusiasm that the preceding expedition had left me, and I wanted to return with a different kind of venture, one that did not involve the pressures of record attempts and film schedules. The result was a threesome, Rob Parker, Julian Walker and myself, joined occasionally by others from America and Grand Bahama when the opportunity arose.

Julian and Rob had been two of the support divers on the Conch Sound attempt, and had emerged as competent explorers in their own right. We all wanted to get back to the Bahamas, and directed much time and effort into achieving this, using the success of the 1982 film as a springboard. Support for the venture had come steadily in; it was gratifying to find that many others thought our aims as exciting and worthwhile as we did. The final seal on the 1983 expedition was given by that old friend of British cave-diving, Wookey Hole Caves. The management of the show caves, where cave-diving had started almost fifty years before, had continued to take an interest in the developing sport. Having established the world's only cave-diving museum in their show cave complex, they decided they would like to sponsor our explorations at East End.

The search for a temporary home, a base camp, found us on the floor of the schoolroom at MacLean's Town. If nothing else, this assured us of an early start. Gear had to be got ready each morning before a horde of interested little fingers came into play!

Bahama sunrise. A thousand cicadas say so, and an aged and asthmatic cockerel concurs. Time to hug the sheet and pretend sleep. Overnight, the airbed has given up the struggle, and the hard concrete floor of the schoolroom makes a comfortless couch. We bluff each other into making breakfast: a slap ends the high whine of an errant mosquito and Julian knows we know he is awake. Rob and I watch the pot go on and think of rising.

Each morning someone would lose this getting-up game, and a breakfast of sorts would be prepared while the others fought the sandflies around the outside tap. Empty line reels would be refilled, a laborious task which involved winding several hundred metres of nylon line around two air-tanks ten metres apart, and then colour-tagging it at each turn before winding it all back on to another reel. We tagged the line at ten metre intervals so that by counting the tags on the return swim, after laying a new stretch of line, we could see how far we had explored. By noting the depth of the passage at each tag, and taking a compass bearing down the line ahead, we could construct a reasonably accurate plan of the new cave. Tagging was also a simple method of increasing safety: instead of a single tag at each turn we used two, one yellow, the other black, twisted into the plait of the rope. The yellow tag always went on the side of the two that would be nearest the entrance, the black on the side that was farthest into the cave. The line can be the only guide to the way out, especially if the water is filled with fine silt, stirred by the current flow or the passage of a diver. It is always possible to become separated from the line in an underwater cave, and there is little to indicate which direction to take if, by luck or good judgment, the line is rediscovered. With a finite supply of air, the chances of survival become slimmer. Our twin-tagging system meant that a ten metre swim at most would lead the diver to a direction sign. If a yellow tag appeared first, then the diver would be swimming into the cave. If a black tag appeared, he would be heading out.

Line-tagging was a boring task but, with the number of new caves we were exploring, it became a necessary chore almost every day. Each reel held about two hundred metres of thick line, strong enough to cope with the abrasive force of the currents in the ocean holes.

With the gadgetry of exploration clean and complete, a gaggle of village children would assist us down to the boat each morning. Sometimes two or three fresh mangoes would appear in a shy and tiny hand, or a fresh loaf of sweet Bahamian bread, still warm from the oven. Whether these were thank you gifts for keeping the kids occupied,

10 Rob Parker enters the deep cleft of Lothlorien

11 Daylight streams into the vast underground hall of Lothlorien from two of its five entrances

12 (*left*) Dr George Benjamin, who masterminded the earliest blue holes exploration, prepares to dive in a South Andros blue hole

13 (*below*) Deep in an inland blue hole in South Andros, a diver examines a fossilised star coral in the limestone wall of the cave, a relic of shallow Bahamian seas of a million years ago

14 (*opposite right*) Martyn Farr prepares to dive, with three torches and side-mounted tanks

15 (*opposite below*) Martyn Farr with some of the twenty-three tanks used on the final Conch Sound push

16 (*left*) Rob Parker explores a cave passage that water has hollowed out along a vertical fault line

17 (*below*) A diver moves through the halocline, mixing fresh and saline layers in a shimmering, cloud-like blur

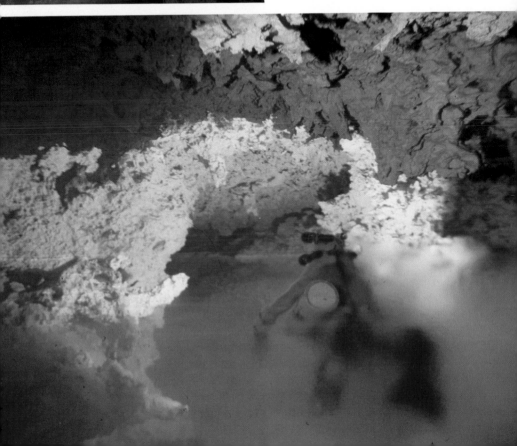

or whether our apparent poverty made the villagers feel sorry for us, we could never quite work out.

MacLean's Town is quite literally the end of the road on Grand Bahama. Here, the potholed track from Freeport bows to the myriad of tidal creeks and mangrove swamps, and onward travel is by sea alone. Once the village was a thriving road end terminal for the ferry to Abaco, the neighbouring island, but with the deterioration of the road, business has virtually disappeared. A distant government has little interest in expensive road repairs, so some of the villagers brave the potholes and make the daily journey to Freeport, and town work, while others live in the old style, conch-fishing or hand-trawling, making an increasingly precarious living from the sea. Conch, once in abundant supply, are now harder to find, over-fished to the point of imminent scarcity. One of the world's largest edible shellfish, their popularity as a Bahamian delicacy has led to a fearful decline in numbers over the years. High piles of bleaching shells, each with a distinctive hole where the conch has been dislodged, form a pink, skeletal shoreline beside the piers of any Bahamian community.

The headmaster took school assembly on the dusty playground as we stowed the last of the gear. The muffled purr of the Johnson outboard mingled with small voices raised in song as the schoolday started and the pier fell behind. The Zodiac inflatable headed out across the bay, its wake rippling the reflections across the still water.

The coast of eastern Grand Bahama slipped by. By now the names were growing familiar: Rumer's Creek, Deep Water Cay, Big and Little Harbour Creeks, Sweeting's Cay. Simple descriptions of the land, the names of people from its past, words to distinguish one low, flat, rocky shoreline from the next.

Sweeting's Cay stretched eastwards, half-way down the curving end of the main island coast. The settlement of the same name, the last village on the island, lay on the south side of the Cay, a long scattering of brightly-coloured houses along the water's edge. A small boy and four men watched our approach with interest. We tied up next to a small, blue fishing dinghy, the only other boat on the pier, and scrambled ashore. At the end of the concrete jetty, on a vivid pink hut, a large notice said 'Welcome to Sweeting's Cay'. From behind the hut, rhythmic music poured, and the noise and bustle of a community at play filled the air. Today, it seemed, was Independence Day. Everyone was celebrating the nation's release from the bonds of Britain with considerable gusto.

'Blue holes? Hey, yeah, man, they's blue holes roun' here!' A huge, beaming local shook our hands. He led us towards the noise.

In the village square, it became obvious that not only the people of Sweeting's Cay, but half of the population of MacLean's Town were there. Mouthwatering smells came from an oil-drum barbecue on one side; reggae belted from large disco speakers on someone's porch. We crept past, gathering a curious following on the way. They all knew about blue holes – wasn't there a big one down by the 'missel base' (The U.S. Space Tracking Station)?

There was, the Lucayan Caverns, by then the world's most extensive underwater cave-system. We had come to Grand Bahama's East End in the hope of finding a similar network of passages, an extensive horizontal maze, filled with delicate crystal formations, the relics of dry spells when the now-submerged caves were exposed to the air of the ice ages.

The Lucayan Caverns had been explored over a period of years by American cave-divers, including Dennis Williams, who had slowly extended their explorations to cover a staggering ten kilometres of interconnected passages, a maze of tunnels in the limestone bedrock of the island barely twenty metres below the surface.

So, looking for another such impressive natural curiosity, we followed a small boy from Sweeting's Cay through the thick tangle of undergrowth behind the village, carefully avoiding the poisonwood bushes and tugging our legs free of the clinging 'love-vines' which caught at our feet.

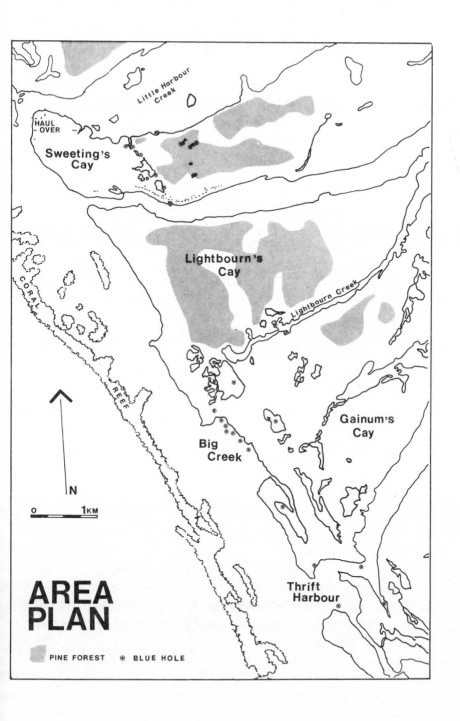

AREA
PLAN

PINE FOREST ◉ BLUE HOLE

Little Harbour Creek

HAUL-OVER

Sweeting's Cay

CORAL

REEF

Lightbourn's Cay

Lightbourn Creek

Gainum's Cay

Big Creek

N

0   1KM

Thrift Harbour

Through the interlacing branches we could see the gleam of water. In a few moments we stood at its edge, looking out over a wide and shallow saltwater lake. The small boy grinned enthusiastically and pointed to the water's edge.

'They's a blue hole theah, man,' he said. His older companions pointed out others around the lake. It still had not dawned on them that we intended diving these and a look of complete incredulity came over their faces as Julian attached a regulator to the small tank we had carried over with us and I prepared to enter the water.

'Hey, you ain't goin' in theah, man? Thay's dangerous, you mebbe get caught down theah, never come out!'

'Man, they's big fish in theah!'

'Hey, you tell me if you see any crawfish!'

The final comment was more true to life. Having realised that we were definitely going to do it, someone decided we must have an ulterior motive. Crawfish, the Bahamian lobster, makes good eating. Like conch, it too is getting scarce where people live.

'They used to be BIG crawfish in theah. We ain't seen them nowadays, maybe they all go somewhere.' Maximum sustainable yield is an unknown concept in communities that have always made a good, easy living from the sea. Little additions like outboard motors and tourist demand can make a big difference in a generation, speeding up the process of fishing beyond the capacity of the seas to provide.

Underwater we entered another, eerie world, a world of dim translucent light, where long tendrils of maroon and pale green algae grew down into the mouths of caves. Here, there were no sharp outlines, no rock, no stone, only an all-pervading clear green glow.

Caves there were, but out of a fey and ghostly world, with entrances such as we had never seen before. Tiny silver fish hung motionless in the algal fronds, pale anemones reached out with long, lacy tendrils in search of minute prey. If caves ever seemed like entrances to the Other World, these were they. As I drifted down into the darkness, delicate strands of algae, disturbed by my bubbles, came with me and enclosed me in a cloud. Without a torch I could see little, though enough to tell me that the slope continued down out of the range of filtered sunlight. I floated up to rejoin the group.

The villagers began to get enthusiastic and tales of other entrances in the lake bubbled out faster than we could note them down. We spent an hour or so swimming around the shallow lake, pin-pointing them all. Some were large and open, others merely crevices beneath the overhanging sides, full almost to their roofs with fine organic debris. It seemed that the lake, a geological curiosity, was once the roof of a gigantic cavern network that had long ago given up the fight with gravity and collapsed. The neat, vertical sides and the flat, smooth floor supported this theory. A Cuban geologist, Nuñez Jimenez, has produced an explanation of this upheaval, which he calls aston development.

Aston collapse occurs when the roof of a cave which has formed underwater suddenly has the buoyant support of that water removed – as would happen when the sea-level fell during the ice ages. In some cases, where cracks and joints in the overlying limestone have already been enlarged by flowing water, or by contraction of the rock as the land dries out, the roof is sufficiently weakened to collapse into the passage below. In the almost perfectly horizontal layers of Bahamian limestone this can have a domino effect, with each layer collapsing into the void left by the one below, until the final surface layer goes too. The result is a large, often circular, hole in the ground.

This is one of the ways in which entrances to blue holes form and sometimes there is a gap down the side of the collapse that is large enough for divers to squeeze through to reach the continuation of the original cave beyond. The lake behind Sweeting's Cay settlement could well be a massive aston collapse, several hundred metres long and over one hundred wide. We looked into no less than ten cave entrances leading off the sides of the lake, and we could only hope that some of these were large enough to get through with our bulky diving equipment to explore the caverns beyond.

Hauling ourselves back into the forest undergrowth, a cheerful voice informed us that behind the trees at the northern end of the lake was a second, even larger body of water. By now we had an expanding audience which was not going to let us go before taking us there.

The second lake stretched into the distance, branching into two bays at the far end. Rob Parker swam along the nearshore, looking down shaft after shaft beneath the overhanging shrubbery. We were beginning to feel a little concerned about the extent of the methodical exploration we were faced with in these incredible saline, algal lakes. The locals were only getting into their stride. On the far north shore of the Cay, beyond the second lake, was a little creek with more caves in it. We had seen those from the air and we promised to examine them later. Julian was dragged away to look at some smaller pools while Rob and I went to see two 'boilin' holes' in the creek by the pier.

We walked back through fields, clearings in the forest where cassava and cucumbers had been planted in soil-filled hollows in the rock. The surface of the area was classic limestone pavement, an irregular network of cracks and joints that divided asymmetrical lumps of rock from each other, as though a giant had tried crazy paving but had forgotten to fill in the gaps between the blocks. In geological terms, the blocks are called 'clints' and the gaps between them are 'grykes'. In the Bahamas, the biggest grykes are 'banana holes', a place where deeper soils accumulate in the solutional hollows. Mango trees sheltered the clearings, smaller trees held limes and papaya while here and there small stands of maize showed ripening cobs. All grew out of soil a few centimetres thick at most, their roots searching out cracks in the rock filled with the decaying remains of the previous year's growth.

We walked along the settlement's one street, a concrete

track that ran alongside the creek. The Community had no vehicles and the street was a centre for village life, a meeting place for talk and play, somewhere to sit out and exchange gossip, have your hair plaited, or sit and watch time go by. A boy sat on a roof playing a guitar. Three old men looked up from a card game and grinned. Beside them, oblivious to all, a baby girl slept in a milk crate with her thumb in her mouth, under a blue plaid shawl.

The blue holes in the creek were only a few metres offshore but there was no chance of us diving them. A few years before, a village girl had been playing with her friends in the currents of the cave mouth and had been drowned. Conch shells had been piled into the entrance to make sure that no one became trapped again. We could see water welling up between the shells, forming a cold mound of water among the mangroves. Later in the day, the current would reverse as tidal pressures changed. The inflow had been strong enough to pull the young girl down.

The Bahamian who showed us the holes could remember the incident. When they blocked up the cave, he said, water burst from a small hole behind a nearby house and swept across the street to the sea. This happened a few times before the hole in the creek unblocked itself enough to restore the equilibrium and settle the tidal pattern again.

Bewildered by the complexity and profusion of the underwater caverns that must underlie the Cay, we left. Assured that we would soon return, our guides shouted goodbyes from the quay and went off to rejoin the party. There was still time for us to run the Zodiac round to the north side of Sweeting's Cay and look for the caves in the small creek there. The tide was rising and we made quick time to the sea. Running inside the fringing reef, we rounded the point at Haul Over, a small collection of expatriate houses where a barking dog was the only sign of life, and entered the long channel of Little Harbour Creek.

From the creek the tangled, interlacing mangroves looked impenetrable. We cruised past, blissfully unaware of the small opening that led into the little creek we were searching for. It took a long time to trek round and discover the creek from behind, a hot and irritating stumble over broken swash and thick pine scrub. The flat expanse of Sweeting's Cay gave little clue from the ground of distant features and it took Julian shinning up a tree to rediscover water.

First we came to a landlocked lake, a shallow oval much smaller than either of the other lakes. At the southern end the water had a distinctive blueness that suggested cave. We peered in, taking turns with the single set of mask and fins we had brought along with us. It looked narrow, but clear enough for exploration, and we hoped there would be an easier route to haul gear across from the boat. From the tree, Julian had seen the second of the two big lakes, only a few hundred metres to the south. We had come almost full circle and it was possible that there might be some sort of underground link between this small lake and the distant one.

The short walk from the lake to the creek, although only a hundred metres or so, was atrocious. We stumbled over limestone pavement that rain and acid waters had corroded into a sharp and jagged landscape, half-obscured by mud and water. A careless step and an ankle could easily be broken, or skin torn to ribbons. Dried and ancient pine stumps littered the land; small scrubby thorns vied with encroaching mangroves and sharp, parched grass for the little nourishment the soil could offer. It was inhospitable ground. In the near distance, tall Bahamian pines offered vertical relief, although there was no relief of movement in their thick understorey. There, agave, vines, poisonwood and thatch palm were even more resistant to human passage. The ankle-breaking limestone barrens still proved to be the easier option.

The little creek, however, was beautiful. Pushing our way through the thick final barrier of mangroves, we stepped into cool, waist-deep water. Small fish darted into cover in the branching roots, and the crisp skeletons of calcareous algae crunched beneath our feet. The blue holes lay at the end of the channel, as though the creek had decided to make a 90° turn and plunge away from the sun. In effect, it had. The clean, calcareous floor was a sign of strong currents, and the only continuation was into the caves, the underground tidal channels.

After the sapping heat of the scrubland, it came as an immense relief to plunge into the clear water. Surrounded on all sides by screening mangroves, the creek was a small enclosed world of its own, a comforting retreat from the flat expanse of the Cay. Sunlight filtered through the green canopy of leaves, playing chase with the shadows in the underwater roots. A small school of black and yellow sergeant-majors returned from hiding to bask in the sun, and bright-red damselflies danced in the leaves. The place was a secret gem. I waded thigh-deep down the creek towards the sea, leaving the others behind.

Pushing past a low branch, I met another junction. Moving upstream in a different direction, I idly explored the new channel, enjoying the stillness and paying more attention to the complex geometry of the mangrove roots than to the ground beneath my feet. And so I nearly fell into the deep hole at the end, having lifted my gaze further to look at the distant trees through a break in the tangled bushes.

The blue hole was almost ten metres long, a sudden abrupt stop which took up the entire end of the creek from side to side. I pulled the mask up from round my neck and peered underwater. Floating above the narrow entrance chasm, I let my eyes slowly adjust to the darkness below.

The curious thing about all these entrances in the shallow creek was that all the life we could see from the surface bore little relation to that of the surrounding mangrove waters. It more resembled the colourful and varied life of the offshore reef. Angelfish swam sedately from one side to the other, gliding along the walls in serene elegance. Small crawfish peered from crevices, half-obscured by multi-coloured, many-shaped corals and sponges. Tiny damselfish glared belligerently from their scraps of territory and, further down in the shadows, a school of rainbow parrotfish swam, a colourful presence in the deeper cave.

The juxtaposition of these two environments, mangrove and marine, was almost surreal. What we might find in the darkness, in the unexplored cave, was still a mystery.

But the sun was taking its toll of enthusiasm. It had been too long a day, a ridiculous day, almost. We'd seen over thirty new caves and were now spoilt for choice. We splashed down the little creek to rejoin the main one, and floundered through muddy shallows to recover the Zodiac from its upstream mooring.

On the long ride back to MacLean's Town we were quieter than usual, exhausted by the day's rigours. I sat in the bow, looking thoughtfully at the flickering, half-seen reef below. We know so little of the world we inhabit and, despite all the physical and technological achievements of mankind, there is so much left to explore.

4

Aquarius, the Waterbearer

We needed a way of identifying the caves we knew on Sweeting's Cay. The local villagers had no name for them, or for the three lakes. In the dim light of the schoolhouse that evening, we held a christening session. The lakes we named with little imagination but impeccable logic. One, Two and Three, south to north. With beer to stimulate prose, we called the little creek on the north shore Zodiac Creek, and the caves the Zodiac Caverns, after our little boat. The generator stuttered to a halt, out of fuel, and we went to bed, Rob and Julian to luxurious foam slabs pulled from the ruins of the old schoolhouse next door and shaken thoroughly to remove fleas, sandflies and other infestations. On balance, I felt better off with my leaking air mattress on the hard floor.

Next morning we returned to the creek, the higher tide allowing us the luxury of hauling the boat inside its sheltering greenery. Regulators were fitted to tanks already set in our special side-harnesses, and these were lowered into the water, to be strapped on where weight was less of a problem. Lights were checked and helmets donned. Buoyancy jackets, to compensate for our changing weight at different depths, were slipped over our heads and secured. The process was methodical, carried out carefully step by step to ensure no margin for error.

Cave-divers in Britain have evolved a solo ethic for exploration. This is frowned on in sport scuba diving, where divers usually pair up for safety. While the hazards confronted in the open sea can often be minimised by joint effort, those encountered in the depths of a cave may often be better dealt with alone. Two divers in danger, in zero visibility, perhaps in low and tight passages, could be two people dying together. Diving alone in such conditions removes the responsibility for another's safety from the exploring diver and leaves him to concentrate on his own.

To compensate for this self-dependence, the cave-diver carries an elaborate life-support system. A minimum of two air tanks is mandatory, one on each hip, each with its own breathing regulator and a gauge to say how much air remains in the tank at any point during the dive. When the first tank is emptied of one-third of its air on the inward swim, the diver changes regulators underwater, now breathing air from the other tank. When a third of that too has gone, it is time to turn round and begin the exit. Only one-third of the total air supply is used on the inward journey. If a sudden failure of one regulator occurs, there is still enough air remaining in the other tank to get the diver out, provided nothing else goes wrong. Even if no further difficulties are met on the way out, the changeover from one tank to the other is repeated, thus ensuring there is always an even balance of air in each system to deal with any emergencies that may arise. If the diver becomes entangled in the guideline, or loses it altogether, or if in zero visibility it has dragged to one side into a low section where he might get physically stuck, extra air is necessary to allow time to deal with the situation. There are techniques, of course, for overcoming the most serious difficulties, given adequate experience and a cool head. The stress of such situations, however, even for a highly-experienced cave-diver, increases the breathing rate considerably. Even the reserve of a spare third in each tank is sometimes cutting it fine, but the 'Third's Rule' has become one of the primary tenets of international cave-diving, whatever the circumstances.

Two years before, while exploring Conch Sound Blue Hole, Martyn Farr changed regulators underwater, 700 metres into the cave, after placing a staging tank deep inside in readiness for the final attempt on the end the next day. He was wearing four tanks, with a separate regulator on each. Switching to his fourth, unused, tank, he discovered that the regulator had malfunctioned and was useless. Gasping for air, he changed back and without further ado turned for the entrance, almost three-quarters of a kilometre away, secure in the belief that he had enough air in his three remaining tanks to get him out. But he was moving too quickly, already under the strain of knowing that a vital part of his life-support system had failed. Before he had gone more than a couple of hundred metres, a loop of the guideline caught in the backset he was wearing. Try as he might, he had no way of freeing himself from this second predicament other than the last desperate step of cutting the line itself! By then extremely worried, it took two attempts to get a knife free before he was able to cut himself out of the tangle. He had very little air to spare at all when he reached Rob Parker, who had noticed the jerking on the line, and had come to see what was wrong. Martyn, one of the world's most experienced cave-divers, emerged from the dive badly shaken after such a close reminder of his own mortality.

So the cave-diver equips himself to survive. A set of accurate gauges reveals depth, direction and air supply. Watch and decompression tables enable him to calculate the dive profile, the set of depth-and-time-related rules that enable decompression sickness, the bends, to be avoided. A helmet protects his head from the rock roof and at least three torches are carried to avoid the possibility of light failure which could leave the diver blind in the depths of the underwater cave. Add to this the reel of guideline (and a smaller spare in case the main line is lost, and has to be searched for), and all the standard gear of a scuba diver and more, and you have an underwater spaceman, a speleonaut, floating at the end of an umbilical cord that leads back down the dark corridors to the world outside. Complete in his mobile life-support system, he intends to stay alive if things go wrong.

Diving alone in such circumstances is an acceptable danger. You are more aware of the potential hazards, readier to overcome them, more conscious of the responsibility of looking after yourself. Even then it is only with considerable experience and training that underwater, underground exploration can be carried out with relative safety. There are many rules to be learned but there is no substitute for experience. Enough tragic statistics are available to prove it.

Julian, the first to find the creek, wanted to dive the cave he had found in the corner of the final bend, a clear opening overhung by mangroves and teeming with fish. Rob Parker was keen on a slightly bigger entrance just beyond it, while I wanted to explore the entrance that I had found at the end of the side channel. All fell neatly into place, without any haggling over priorities. With nervous excitement we entered the water.

Moving up the shallow inlet was a little more difficult in the heavy diving gear and, with a full wetsuit on, I was soon sweating profusely. It was more with relief than anticipation that I arrived at the cave and allowed myself to float down into its cool, enveloping embrace.

The cavern entrance was narrow; it took two or three attempts to find a route wide enough to descend, zig-zagging across the largest parts of the shaft. I paused long enough to allow my eyes to adjust to the gloom, and to tie my guideline to the most substantial rock I could find. The walls around were thick with life, marine plants and animals that seemed to find conditions here ideal for survival, drawing their food from the rich inflowing current that swept through the mangrove roots above. A tiny cleaner-shrimp scurried backwards behind a boulder, unused to such a large and noisy intruder.

Fourteen metres down, I hit bottom, still in a narrow rift

barely wide enough to twist from side to side and look around. On my right, the passage seemed to close down. On my left, heading south, it was wider, though hardly inviting. Pausing long enough to ensure my line was firmly belayed at the bottom of my descent route, I moved on, trailing the line behind, and using my fingers to pull gently along the wall. To make sweeping fin-strokes would be to churn up a cloud of mud, ruining any chance I had of seeing the way on.

Within a few metres, the passage made an abrupt 90° twist, becoming low, wide and oval, hollowed out between two horizontal beds of rock. It was barely a metre high, leaving little room to swim between the roof and the soft sediments below. I finned delicately forward and the passage began to enlarge.

It is often easier to visualise the shape and size of a passage after a dive than when you are exploring it for the first time. All a cave-diver can see, even in the very clearest waters, is confined within the narrow reach of his lights. A certain tunnel vision inevitably occurs. Photographs cannot adequately convey the physical and emotional feeling of such underwater exploration, the sense of isolation, of claustrophobic concern as the darkness closes in behind you. You move in a small, isolated world of your own, illuminated in a tiny pool of light, linked to the outside world only by the thin nylon cord which runs back through the labyrinth to the sun. Your perception alters, you become unusually aware of your breathing and your heartbeat, and all that is going on immediately around you. Senses readjust. Sight and sound are impaired, taste and smell irrelevant, touch all-important. A sixth sense of awareness is working overtime, keyed in to the unexpected. You are entirely, utterly, alone.

The cave grew in size, its walls smoothed by the currents that pulsed in and out in an unending rhythm. At the moment a gentle outflow was keeping the water ahead clear, blowing what sediments I was disturbing back towards the entrance. White sponges or 'dead man's fingers' hung from the roof in globular profusion. Tiny hydroids clung to the rock walls, competing for space above the encroaching anemones and sponges. In crevices along the sides, the long feelers of crawfish were an indicator of impressive size. Mangrove leaves littered the floor, most of which seemed to be composed of the same white algal skeletons that formed the bed of the creek, oatmeal-shaped flakes of *Halicona*, whose living forms clung to the underwater mangrove roots. The passage teemed with life wherever I looked, confounding the image of caves as cold and lifeless places. All this complex, thriving community managed to exist in total darkness, drawing nourishment from the debris of the inflow, or from luckless companions of the night that strayed too near the range of rival mouths.

Where possible, I belayed the line to rocks or boulders, keeping it down the widest section of the passage. The cave shrank on either side to a few low centimetres and I could not risk the line floating free and dragging into one of those low areas. I had no way of telling how much my movements were disturbing the clarity of the water and I was a little apprehensive; if I had to return in a blackout, I wanted to be sure that the line was safe to follow.

By now I was well into the cave. It showed no signs of closing down, unlike many before. Looming up out of the darkness, a huge pillar of rock split the passage before me, an old crystalline formation from the distant past of the cave, joining roof and floor. My line ran out just as I reached it, and I hung beside it in the water, one hand on its pitted, brown surface, the other on the reel. Time, and a million burrowing organisms, had reduced the smooth calcite surface to a rough, uneven coat. Fine silt lay in crannies, and soft sponges clung to the rugged outer layer. Beyond the pillar the cave continued and the urge to leave the line and swim on was almost irresistible.

I stayed by the pillar for several moments, lost in the shadowy mystique of the cave. Small red mites moved in the sand around the base of a cluster of stalagmites, little

18 Rob Parker and Julian Walker tag line outside the village
school

19 Surveying Zodiac Creek

20 Aquarius, where the tidal creek goes underground

21 Rob Palmer swims through Hinchliffe Hall. Sponges and serpulid worm tubes festoon the walls and roof

22 Rob Palmer in the entrance passage of Aquarius. Pendulous white sponges hang from the roof

23 The stalagmite column that marked the end of the first dive in Aquarius

24 The smaller American reels were easier to handle in currentless caves

alien beings in a strange city of towering stone, threatened by the encroaching sand of a pale desert. The cave was still under two metres high, sloping off to the side over banks of sculptured sand, patterned by the currents of the moon.

The water was blowing gently out and on the return I let it do most of the work, using my hands and fins only to control direction. At the entrance I twisted upwards and worked my way out of the shaft, scattering the fish again, to spit my mouthpiece out in the bright sunlight. Sight and sound flooded back. I pulled my mask down and breathed in to the raucous cry of a startled heron in the mangroves. The scents of the outside world were thick and sweet.

High on adrenalin, I splashed round to see what the other two had found. Rob's entrance, which had seemed so promising, was bare. An underwater search yielded no guideline, only jumbled boulders and silt. Julian's was tied to a branch over the hole, so I followed it down, only to meet Rob coming out. We conducted a brief underwater mime; they too had run out of line, and were on their way back. Julian's lights appeared in the darkness behind Rob as we moved out.

Their cave was smaller than mine, so I persuaded them to return with me and explore beyond the massive column. We had only been underwater a short time and had plenty of air left in our tanks. Collecting our final reel from the boat, we splashed in convoy back along the creek.

We congregated at the end of the line, and the new reel was fastened on. A silent chorus of O.K. signs and we were off, moving into new territory in single file. I led, with Rob close behind, while Julian brought up the rear, a less than happy position with two sets of fins in front, spoiling his view. We soon came to an obvious split in the cave. Straight ahead, the passage continued, a curving channel barely half-a-metre high between the mire on the floor and the roof above. A more appealing passage led off to our left, large enough for the three of us to explore safely. We swam down a slope, into deeper, colder water, and a sudden change.

65

Here, the water took on an incredible clarity, a blue translucence that faded into the distance beyond reach of our lights. Moving through the centre of a series of stalagmite-filled halls, we were able to make out every detail, each curious shape in the rock, each nook, each cranny, each turn and twist of the cave. The tidal flow and its cloudier waters had been left behind and we flew gingerly from chamber to chamber. Moving in this part of the cave bore little relation to swimming.

One room contained a graceful column over three metres high . . . but only five centimetres in diameter! We were terrified of catching such a slender formation on our equipment, destroying in seconds what it had taken nature æons to achieve. Care saw us through to a final chamber, 230 metres from the entrance and twenty metres down. We could find no further way on. Even here life survived. Tiny sponges, barely a cubic centimetre in size, clung to formations and walls, specks of colour on the brown uniformity. Serpulid fan-worms left delicate Celtic spirals of calcite tube across the stone, ending in a spray of fine tentacles that slowly, so slowly, filtered the still waters of the cave for food. And there, in a low solutional pocket, floored with white sand, in the very farthest corner of the cave, hung a small white fish, *Lucifuga spelæotes*, the blind cave fish of the Bahamas.

After days of waiting, and looking in cave after cave, we had begun to see what we were looking for. Rob was grinning behind his mask, and Julian gave a thumbs-up sign, and blew a long stream of bubbles that ran in mercurial pools along the roof above. Back in the under-water half-light, before surfacing, we checked our time. We had spent over an hour exploring and so needed to wait for four impatient minutes before surfacing. As we came up, happy and excited, Rob turned to me and grinned.

'Now *that*,' he said, 'was what I came four thousand miles to find.'

Back at our schoolhouse base, we were having trouble

with our air compressor. It had been borrowed from a friend in Nassau and it hadn't been run for a year or so. It would pump air at only half its normal rate, which meant that filling the tanks was becoming a time-consuming grind. We tried stripping carburettor and filters, and double-checking all the seals, but nothing seemed to improve its performance. We now began to worry about the dependability of our air supply.

By nine o'clock, in the insect-ridden darkness, our tanks were full. Julian, tired and disgruntled, staggered in with the last of the load. No one said much but we broke a few cans from our meagre store of beer and quietly celebrated the day while we wrote our diaries, cleaned cameras and checked regulators. In the dim glow of our single bulb, to the irregular thump of the schoolhouse generator and the cry of nightbirds, we started work on the survey of the caves.

Julian's cave, Scorpio, veered away to the east of the creek as soon as it was underwater. It headed straight for the smallest of the three lakes. The cave led to a low, wide chamber, with stalagmites emerging from the silt on either side, and it continued in the same fashion for as far as his lights could reach.

We called my cave Aquarius, because of the strong water flow, and it ran due south of the creek. At the junction of the passages the deep tunnel swung east and the clear passage came to an end only a few metres from the blocked entrance that Rob Parker had attempted to explore. It looked as if Scorpio could be the continuation of the deeper cave in Aquarius, but a partial aston collapse many tens of thousands of years ago had completely blocked the way through.

Now the tease was: what lay across the low chamber in Scorpio, and through the other low passage at the Aquarius crossroads?

By noon next day, Rob and I were back again, floating above the silt banks by the crossroads, both apprehensive about the passage before us. The gap was narrow and claustrophobic, easy enough to negotiate had it been on the surface, or in a dry cave, but underwater in scuba gear it was an altogether different matter. If it became still lower further in, turning round would be difficult. Whatever happened, it would be impossible to keep the water clear. On our left, the line curved down into yesterday's cave. Up here, in the current and the mud, visibility was less spectacular.

Procrastination was pointless. With a small wave, Rob disappeared to try his luck with a passage on the right. I fumbled with my reel, trying to loop it on the old line, but it seemed to have a mind of its own. Coils floated off, ensnaring equipment and drifting in the current. Nervousness was making me clumsy, un-coordinated. I started again, put the line back on the reel, tied the knot properly and moved ahead, making sure that the line lay correctly and looking for the biggest gap over the dune.

There was no easy way. I felt myself being forced left, towards the deeper cave. The wall of the passage came into view; was there enough room to squeeze along that? Unreeling the line awkwardly, at the end of an outstretched arm, I squirmed into the gap, thinking I could worm my way through. The roof came down and caught at the lights on my helmet. Air tanks struck the rock repeatedly, a series of metallic clangs that echoed the tumult of exhausted air from my regulator. My chest ploughed a furrow in the soft silt, pushing a bow-wave of mud in front of me. The world turned brown.

I stopped and closed my eyes, listening to a pounding heartbeat. I was doing it all wrong, clumsily out of tune. Should I go on or would it be better to turn back while I still could? I opened my eyes again and the water was clear. Was the cave getting higher? Perhaps my mind was playing tricks with hope.

The current on my face must come from somewhere. Two more metres, then I would run away. I pushed on the floor and silt billowed up again. It seemed foolish, too great a risk. Was I jamming myself in, digging an underwater grave? Caves don't kill people, stupidity does.

Then, suddenly, it was over. A vast hall was there before me, unfathomable, immense! Towering pillars of rock rose from an unseen floor, the walls fell away on either side, the roof reared to a stone sky. I hung over a lip of sand, my legs in a vice, my head in space. Time moved slowly, the world around me changed, and perspective returned.

The sense of being free was intoxicating. I looped the line over the point of a stalagmite and twisted around to look at the mammoth cavern. The only wall I could see was the one beside me. Follow the wall, see where it leads, I told myself audibly.

The floor undulated up and down, dunes of fine silt piled high against fallen blocks. Stalactites hung from the roof, singly and in clusters. Across the surface of the dunes small crab trails ran in patterned roadways and stalagmites rose in castellated splendour above a landscape of brown valleys and barren downland. Another wall floated into view, closing in with each stroke of my fins. The chamber ended and became a passage, high and wide and crystal clear.

I stopped in the entrance to the new section, tying the line in a firm belay. The shadows danced around me as Rob caught me up. His arm waved out, indicating the chamber. Behind his mask, his eyes gleamed with pleasure. His route could not have gone far, and I felt a slight twinge of guilt at having picked the plum again.

The way ahead was tall and narrow, following the line of an ancient fault. The character of the cave changed with it and the water again took on the blue transparency we had encountered earlier. This time, however, it was accompanied by an intangible aura of menace.

The walls looked as though they might collapse at any moment. Huge, sharp blocks of limestone stood poised on fragile ledges. With every exhalation the rising stream of exhausted bubbles would dislodge a rain of white fragments. We moved with extreme caution, trying to keep as far from the walls as we could. I tied the line to anything that looked solid – and there was little of that – and fought shy of tugging the knots to check them in case the whole wall collapsed. Soon we came to an area where it had.

A massive block leaned drunkenly sideways to fill the passage. A tiny gap beneath it looked barely big enough to squeeze through. Rob waited while I floated carefully down to the opening and – very gently – pushed through. I emerged in open cave again, no less fragile, but big enough to move in easily. Occasional shafts in the floor plunged down to invisible depths, narrow and more confined than the squeeze. I ignored them and concentrated on the cave I could see, as the reel in my hand turned faster. The line spun out to its end by a rock pillar in the centre of the cave. A gentle tug in my hand told me I could go no further. In front, the cave went on, high and narrow and loose, disappearing into blueness.

There was no enticement to swim on this time. I was glad to stop. I clung to the pillar, tying a Gordian knot that would never come undone, before changing regulators and moving back down the passage to rejoin Rob at the squeeze. We surveyed out, leaving a dotted line hung with question marks as we crossed the huge chamber, in touch with only one wall. The void stretched off eastwards, a dark secret.

As we decompressed, I realised with a detached curiosity that I had barely noticed the return through the low bedding. Either the line had floated into a higher route or I had been particularly out of touch on the way in. Probably the latter, but one of the reassuring things about diving alone is that no one can see your mistakes. Stupidity is a little more bearable without an audience.

Julian had managed to get a few metres further into Scorpio before the cave became too low to continue. Drying off in the afternoon sun, Rob and I decided that he must now be under the near end of Lake Three – 'Aston Martin', in our colloquial expedition slang. This still contained an unexplored cave and, despite the obvious surface collapse that formed the lake and blocked the cave, there might be a connection with the more distant Lake Two. Rob, pointing out that he was losing out in the exploration stakes, laid immediate claim to it.

The tide was running out, and we barely managed to extract the Zodiac from its namesake creek. It was a long walk before we reached water deep enough to start the engine and head for home. Passing Haul Over, signs of humanity were evident by a large A-frame house next to the beach. We decided to be sociable.

It turned out that two Americans, Jack Rogers and Nick van Laun, owned the A-frame. For them Sweeting's Cay was an occasional retreat from the pressures of civilisation in Florida. Both were keen divers and knew many of the larger blue hole entrances, as well as a few we had not yet come across. Cold beers broke the ice and they were fascinated by our stories of the caves below their weekend island.

The best news was that they owned a compressor and were willing to let us use it while they were in residence. Our own was giving us increasing cause for concern. We would be utterly hamstrung without the means to compress air. They also offered to lend us spare tanks if we should need them. Evening drew in as our fund of stories ran out, and we made our way back to the schoolroom floor and a dinner of freshly-caught snapper. Our problems seemed to recede a little further into the background but the next morning, things began to fall apart again.

To begin with, the outboard motor would not start. It took over an hour, under the baking sun, to finally cajole it into life. It was obviously overheating. Then the compressor finally capitulated in sympathy and I took its offending parts and the outboard down to Freeport in Nick's car. It was three days before I could get back, tired and frustrated, with a working outboard but no compressor. The parts had to be ordered from America and would take several days to arrive.

Rob and Julian had been anything but inactive. Smiling sweetly at the grandmother of one of our schoolhouse gang of hangers-on (holidays had arrived, which made life a little easier), they had somehow managed to borrow a small wooden boat and were exploring two ocean holes near the village, discovering several hundred metres of submarine cave in the process. The Henford Holes – in memory of a local youth who had spent more time than us with his head inside our engine – were a serious proposition, with extremely strong currents. The two divers had each begun their explorations in the caves at slack water, but had almost been physically ejected by the force of the current on their way out. Fortunately the entrances of both caves were deep or they might have had trouble decompressing because of this.

Such a hazard is no joke. One Grand Bahama blue hole, in which both Rob and I had dived before, has currents so strong they almost entirely prohibit exploration. Chimney Cave, near Freeport, has a vertical shaft twelve metres deep as its entrance. Long dives in the system dictate the bottom of this shaft as the depth of the first decompression stop – which is fine. You can wedge yourself in a corner and cower out of the flow. Unfortunately a stop has to be made at six metres as well, in the full force of the current. The only way to survive is to cling with all your strength to handholds on the wall and let your body stream out in the flow. Slip, and you would be swept to the surface, with no chance of getting down again in time. The ascent to three metres, for the final stop, must be made by climbing backwards, upside down, to another ledge, where again one can huddle out of the current. It is terrifying.

The whirlpool on the inflow is strong enough to pull a fully-equipped diver down into the cave – and has done so to careless swimmers in the past. On the outflow, water wells up with such force that it forms a cold mushrooming mound almost a metre high on the surface. The water appears to boil. The reversal is virtually instantaneous. The Chimney is one of the most dangerous of caves.

Before cave-divers produced a scientific explanation for these currents, the native Bahamians had their own.

Monsters! The inflowing current was caused by the in-drawn breath of these terrible creatures — one long, enormous suck. When they breathed out, water boiled to the surface, clear and cold. The bigger the monster, the stronger the current. This leviathan was Lusca, 'him of de hahnds', a terrifying horror, half-eel, half-squid. Stories in the islands, embellished by oral tradition, told of Lusca reaching out tentacles to grasp fishing boats and their crews, hauling the luckless sailors into the gaping maw of the caves. Was there a foundation to their stories? On our own exploration in Conch Sound Blue Hole, on Andros, we used as our underwater base a six metre cabin boat we had found wedged three metres down across the entrance to the cave. Was it a victim of strong currents or the fury of Lusca?

With our compressor useless, Rob and Julian had been decanting air from our large 105 cubic foot tanks into the smaller 80 cubic foot tanks. Two days of serious explora-tion had left stocks low and tomorrow was Nick and Jack's last day on the island. It would be several days before they returned. We gathered every tank we possessed and took them to be refilled. With Nick and Jack's tanks on loan, we had enough air to bridge the gap until our own compressor was repaired.

It was the fourth of July. As the compressor thudded air in the background, we lit a bonfire on the beach and toasted the release of America from the Empire. We had air for the immediate future and could make plans. Rob was for the cave in the small Lake Three, Julian for the marine Henford Holes. I would continue on my own in Aquarius.

5

The Sunless Sea

The walk to Lake Three, carrying diving gear, was far from pleasant. The limestone that lay beneath the obstructive, snagging mangrove roots was as sharp as obsidian. Pools of mud and water hid ankle-wrecking pits, and the treacherous, brittle rock was a nightmare to negotiate in our soft neoprene socks.

In between the broken stones and rockpools, tiny creatures scuttled away at our stumbling footsteps. Minute crabs and translucent sea-slaters lived in the littoral zone, where the highest tides crept among the rocks and turned the broken landscape into a shallow sea. These creatures form the nightshift, when they emerge from crevices to feed on decaying matter among the stones. The noisy disturbance of our passing stirred them into a frenzied search for a safer daylight home.

Above the highwater mark the ground fauna changed and we frightened lizards instead. The Bahamas are home to several species – anoles, curly-tailed lizards, geckoes, and the larger but now rare rock iguana. The tiny anoles that skittered between our feet on Sweeting's Cay are a curiosity, with a third, pineal eye. No one has established what it is for but it is probably incapable of doing other than distinguishing day from night. It might have some relationship to the reptile's breeding cycle, or perhaps something to do with their chameleon-like ability to vary their colour from brown, through grey, to mottled black. When still, they blend perfectly into the arid scrub. We only noticed them when they moved, dancing out of our way across the low thorns.

The three of us carried Rob Parker's gear to a clear patch of rock by the cave entrance in Lake Three, 'Aston Martin'. While Rob was sorting himself out in the heat, Julian and I splashed into the lake for a swim.

The lake was the result of a small aston collapse, its floor a patchwork of flat limestone flakes, large plates of rock that lay one on another like a jumbled deck of cards. We had already worked out that the end of Scorpio lay under the northern extremity of the lake. The cave on the south side would probably lead into the old continuation of Scorpio to the south. Feeling that Scorpio itself had been linked originally to Aquarius before a collapse at the head of Zodiac Creek, then at one time it might have been possible to swim all the way under the island, through to Lake One at least, and probably to the blue holes in the creek beyond. We had hoped originally that this might still be possible. Unfortunately it looked as though we were about 100,000 years too late.

The fauna of the little lake was unlike that of its cousins a few hundred metres away. There were too many tiny herbivorous snails for the algae to grow in equivalent profusion. The little *Cerithium* molluscs covered everything, grazing on what algae was present like a herd of tiny, spirally-shelled sheep. Small schools of silver mosquito fish lingered in the shallowest fringes of the lake, feeding on the writhing mass of mosquito larvae at the water's edge.

The mosquito fish is a splendid creature which, it has been suggested, has done more to make the Bahamas habitable by man but not by mosquitoes than any other living thing, so efficient is it at removing the pest during its larval stage. Good work for a fish whose Latin name, *Gambusia manni*, means 'worthless'! Its enormous food consumption is vital for its rapid breeding cycle; a pair of mosquito fish could be responsible for over 15,000 young a year if they try hard. Fortunately for mosquitoes, the fish is itself a part of an avian food chain, forming a staple diet for herons and kingfishers. Everywhere there was water, we found these adaptable fish – in pools between stones in the littoral zone, in saline lakes, in freshwater puddles and in tidal creeks.

Rob's path into the cave lay down the side of the collapsed rock flakes, dropping steeply away from the entrance and funnelling down into a low gap between the roof and rock floor. Rob squeezed his way through a forty-centimetre high constriction into Gemini, the third Zodiac Cavern. Moving away from the collapse zone of the entrance, he swam into a cave that grew slowly in size. Soon he was swimming among formations again. These grew increasingly profuse, and the cave grew wider and wider, until the walls were completely out of range of the beams of his lights. He wove a zig-zag course across the cave, swimming slowly from one group of columns to the next, occasionally seeing one wall or the other. At their base, deep pits plunged down to shattered rifts, twice the depth of the chamber. The walls and roof were festooned with delicate formations and the very walls of the cave were covered in places by sheets of flowstone, a thin calcite coat that lay on the rock in a smooth crystalline crust. The once-white calcite was stained a light brown by tannic solutions in the cave water, and gave anchorage to the same type of small sponges and fan-worms that we had seen in Aquarius.

The presence of such delicate formations was an indication that currents had never flowed fiercely in the caves, as they would in an ocean hole. Such strong tidal currents would have worn the fragile speleothems away, or carried so much organic material into the cave that a flourishing marine fauna, burrowing into them, would have altered them almost beyond recognition, if not destroyed them.

Rob's line came to an end before he had crossed the long

chamber and, somewhat stunned by his discovery, he began mapping his way back out.

Our sense of continuing wonder at these caves might need some explanation. In our earlier explorations on Andros, when we had come across underwater speleo-thems for the first time they had seemed amazing. In cold reality, they were somewhat shapeless lumps of rock, overgrown by opportunist fauna to the point of being almost unrecognisable. In Britain underwater formations are so scarce as to be virtually unknown by the majority of cavers. Those that exist are accidental, inundated by some partial blockage that holds back water temporarily in the life of the cave. Even in 'dry' caves it is unusual to find such a plethora of speleothems. For us to discover them in such abundance underwater, in a scarcely changed state, was so exciting and unusual that we waxed somewhat more lyrical than might be expected of the usual macho cave-diver.

In Britain, a few dozen metres might be an acceptable first dive at a new site. Rob had explored two hundred metres, easily, and in an overwhelmingly beautiful cave. The simplicity of it all, and the quality of the surroundings, made our experiences seem surreal.

Such massive chambers make it easier to understand the creation of the lakes. What was becoming increasingly difficult to understand was why, with such wide, gaping caverns at a comparatively shallow depth, there were not more lakes around. Twenty metres is not deep in real terms, it is about the size of a four-storey house. Some of the chambers were much shallower than that. Their roofs were, almost without exception, formed along the bottom of a flat bed of rock. In many places, it was possible to see where slabs had fallen long ago. Some of these even had stalagmites growing on them. All that was holding the rock up (apart from the calcite columns) was the integral strength of the brittle rock itself, and the buoyant support of the water. This led to a new psychological concern: a peculiar blend of agoraphobia and claustrophobia. Every time we swam into such a place we became acutely aware that we were underground, with uncountable tons of rock over our heads, in a position from which it would be difficult to escape if it caved in. The thought of all that rock above ... all that space around ... Everyone felt more comfortable close to a wall than floating free in the darkness, out of touch with solid ground. Smaller passages, where we could relate better to our surroundings, were less worrying. The fact that the stalagmites had probably been there for at least 40,000 years, and the caves had not collapsed seriously since then, was only theoretical reassurance. Even so, we relished the pure thrill of swimming out suddenly into a big open space, and the sense of mystery that came from looking into the panoramic expanse of darkness beyond.

There was still the matter of what lay beyond the end in Aquarius. Later that day I dived there again. The explored cave had been personified, removing some of the mystery. The chamber was named Hinchliffe Hall, in gratitude for the help given us by John Hinchliffe, a very good friend in Freeport who had put in long hours on our behalf. The long, fractured canyon at the end became the Scorpion's Tail, the side tunnel where we had first encountered *Lucifuga* was Pisces Passage.

The equipment for my Aquarius push would have doubled for a long, deep dive off a wintry Hebrides. Normally a drysuit is as out of place in the Bahamas as an iced Martini is at the South Pole. Experience on long dives beneath Andros had taught us several lessons. The possible length of this dive, the decompression, the chill of the outflowing current, all meant I would need a system that would minimise the gradual loss of body heat that simple thermal conduction would bring in waters only a few degrees below my body temperature. Hypothermia is an unnecessary complication on a long cave dive.

To the membrane drysuit, and thermal undersuit of thinsulate, was added all the complex array of equipment that is part and parcel of long-distance cave-diving.

The end of the existing line was over 200 metres into the cave, at a depth approaching thirty metres, and I hoped to penetrate at least twice as far on this attempt. How deep that would take me, I did not know, but felt that a policy of over-caution was advisable. Two 80 cubic foot tanks would not be enough so a further 105 cubic foot tank was mounted on a backpack and added to the weight already strapped on. Now I was grateful for the warm water of the creek. I could ease the strain by floating back away from the boat, as I made my final adjustments.

Spit in the mask – rinse in the creek. Hold fast to a mangrove branch as first the right fin, then the left fin, goes on. Clip the reel to the harness, check the torches and air supply, and fin gently towards the cave, mentally slowing down the breathing rate.

In the cave half-remembered landmarks appear . . . a sweeping sandbank on the right, a small pattern of red and brown sponges on the left-hand wall. Air continues to crash through the regulator in slow, measured bursts. The tank on my back scrapes the roof as I force myself through the low section. That slight sense of concern accompanies the sudden emergence into the big chamber, even though the move was expected. Shadows flicker in Hinchliffe Hall as I swim across. A tiny sponge-crab scuttles across the floor, its camouflaging mantle of living sponge fooling no one but itself in the eternal night.

The hall comes to an end. The line is coiled twice around a massive stalagmite that marks the entrance to the final passage – my advance camp. Bleeding the air from my suit, I sink to the floor of the cave beside the column of rock. Moving slowly to avoid stirring up the sediment, I slip out of the backpack and clip the large tank to the line. Free of the weight, I rise too fast, hitting the cave roof before I can re-adjust my buoyancy. The tank had been heavier than I thought!

Hand on mouthpiece two, a deep breath, and change. Another little adrenalin spurt until the rush of indrawn air proves that the second regulator works. Check the gauges, adjust the fit, and off, unclipping the new reel as I go.

The line curves down beneath the huge block and the low squeeze brings me out into the final stretch. Finning cautiously down the clear, shattered passage, the terminal knot comes into view. Tie the new line on tight, check the gauges again, clear a few traces of water from my mask. Procrastinate awhile, making a few finicky adjustments to my gear before pushing on.

The cave continues as a high, clear canyon of blue water. I can see everything; the clarity is perfect. A lonely serpulid tubeworm reaches out for whatever microscopic life there is to feed it. It must spend much of its life being hungry. Blind *Lucifuga* haunts the sand on the floor. Ahead, the cave narrows.

The way on is down, through a tiny crevice. I look unhappily at the ridiculous opening. I might fit through, but only just, and only at one particular angle. It will mean forcing myself down feet first because there is no way I could turn round if I got stuck. To come back, I must repeat the precise angle, and so will not be able to return until the water clears enough to allow me to see what to do. With detached commitment, I go.

My chest and back squeeze between solid rock, my tanks scrape through on either side, losing paint in the process. A push, a thrust, a scrape, and through, to see before me a small room, barely big enough to turn in, with only rabbit holes leading on, tiny tubes barely ten centimetres in diameter. I crouch in the room as clouds roll in, clutching the line tightly and wishing I were Alice, with her small bottle of shrinking potion.

I would prefer to forget the upward return through the squeeze; it was a foolish commitment in the first place. It takes a while in the obscuring silt-cloud before I find the proper angle and for a moment I begin to doubt whether I will ever get out. After several futile attempts, I pull free at last and begin the long swim to daylight, an hour away

25 Sweeting's Cay and Lakes One, Two and Three from above, looking north

26 The curving second entrance to Gemini, in Lake Two

27 (*left*) Julian Walker, with American double-hundreds (twin 100 cubic foot capacity tanks), in the Lucayan Caverns entrance

28 (*below*) Swimming through the wide halls of Gemini

29 (*opposite right*) The agoraphobic/claustrophobic caves...

30 (*opposite below*) Stalagmites and stalactites bar the way in a Gemini passage

31 Orchids and dead pine-tree, Lake Three

down the long passages. Disappointment mingles with a distinct sense of relief.

Marine blue holes are really very different from their inland counterparts. Aquarius is an unusual link between the two, not quite one or the other.

With Julian, Rob and I took the Zodiac out of the Henford Holes after our dives in the inland caves. Julian had already explored two hundred metres of passages in Henford Two, and was intent on following up a few last unexplored leads. While he did so, Rob and I went into the cave to take some photographs. It gave me my first chance to see the Henford caves, and to compare them with others.

From the boat the blue hole looked only like a darker patch of sea. Storm clouds were gathering, and the rich colours of sunlight faded to a dull steel-grey. It looked uninspiring from above but underwater it was a different tale.

The entrance was set in an area of sandy shallows, only two or three metres deep. Still in the surge zone, the seascape around the hole was a flat sandy floor, on which grew purple and yellow gorgonians (sea-fans) and flexible sea-rods, all able to withstand the surge and swell by their pliable construction, swaying back and forth with the motion of the sea. Small, robust outcrops of brain and flower coral grew haphazardly among the fans. There was too little shelter on the open seafloor for the more fragile elkhorn and staghorn corals off this exposed tip of Crabbing Point; these would quickly have fallen victim to storm-driven seas from the south.

The seafloor around the Henford Holes was the marine equivalent of terrestrial scrubland, broken here and there by patches of *Thallasia*, dense meadows of seagrass which spread in a thick mat across the floor of this underwater savannah. In the centre, like rich oases, lay the blue holes.

Ocean blue holes create their own environment. Their deeper, enclosing entrances provide shelter for a wide variety of marine life, a hiding place from the hunting ground of the open sea. Not that blue holes are by any means free of predators! In and around the entrance, a diverse community of animals and plants – corals, crustaceans, sponges, anemones, algae and fish – work their way into a habitat that is unusual and complex. Some are there to shelter, some to hunt; some use it temporarily, some make it their permanent abode. Paramount among the latter are sessile communities of hydroids, corals and anemones, and an assorted collection of multi-coloured and many-textured sponges.

These immobile creatures make no distinction between walls or roof – or floor either, when sediments allow. They feed on organic material – plankton and algal fragments, the general rubbish of the sea – brought into the cave on the inflowing current. The inflow is the original free lunch, a concentrated source of nourishment more generous by far than an open seafloor away from the cave. Enough material is carried on the flow to reach hundreds of metres back into the caves, allowing some creatures to exist far from daylight.

As in dry caves, this ability to adapt to different conditions creates a definite zonation in marine caves. The richest zone is in and near the entrance, in the daylight area. Here there is most food, there is sunlight, and there is access to the open sea. There is also competition! Most fish go no further than here, though one or two species make notable exceptions. Some fish are carnivores – snappers, jacks and grunts – a few are herbivores, grazing on the algae that grows around the entrance (algae, being a plant, depends on photosynthesis and cannot live in the darkness inside a cave). Some, like the gaudy parrotfish, are less particular, crunching their way through coral polyps and algae alike, grazing noisily on those members of the entrance community that are unable to run away.

Almost any of the fish off a Bahamian reef can be found in and around the entrance to a blue hole. Squirrelfish linger in crevices, tiny damselfish dart round established territories, defending them against marine inhabitant and cave-diver alike. Angelfish and butterflyfish glide gracefully along narrow gaps in the rock. Schools of jacks and blue-striped grunts are daytime visitors, moving out to hunt in the open sea at night. During the day they grab snacks from the inflowing waters, secure in the shelter of the cave mouth.

Snappers are known to swim into caves and have been seen over 100 metres into ocean holes. Why they should penetrate so far is a mystery. There is more to eat out on the reef, and little in the entrance zone that preys on snapper. Without the sun to say which way is up, they orientate themselves by inbuilt sonar to the nearest solid surface. It is by no means a rare sight to see a snapper swimming along unconcernedly deep into a cave, completely upside-down.

Larger, more spectacular fish frequently visit the caves. Sting-rays are fond of burying themselves in the sand near entrances; once we nearly stepped on three of these in a blue hole in South Mastic Bay on Andros. Moray eels and small octopuses are fond of low crevices and holes in the cave mouths, and nurse sharks occasionally decide to rest in the passages of larger caves.

Paradoxically, though one of the gentlest of the larger sharks, there have been more recorded attacks on man by these sharks than by any other. Maybe these figures should be reversed. Nurse sharks in such attacks have generally been pestered by divers or swimmers intent on demonstrating their bravery to companions. Perhaps it is not too surprising that the shark will, in frustration, turn round and pester its persecutor! Nurse sharks have no teeth, their diet of crustaceans and large shellfish has given them jaws with strong grinding surfaces instead. This does not stop them from giving tormentors a nasty gumming. On the several occasions we have encountered these creatures in ocean caves we have left them to their own devices. Happily, they have returned the favour.

This behaviour does not extend to the other sharks, such

as lemons or black-tips, that are also frequent visitors to blue hole entrances. These have to be left well alone!

A blue hole entrance is really a concentrated coral reef in disguise, a living environment of diverse, brawling communities. This changes as you enter the cave. As the light fades, the bustle stops. The noise of the outside fauna, the clicks, whistles and crunchings, fades away. Night falls. Creatures that shun the daytime reef promenade in full view, secure from predators, in a near to ideal world.

In this transitional zone the walls are a carpet of life, with brightly-coloured sponges, large single coral polyps, jelly-like ascidians and anemones competing fiercely for space, jostling for access to the rich inflowing current. In amongst this covering, feather-duster worms reach out their delicate tubes into the flow, each ending in a bright spray of ethereal tentacles. Encrusting shells make their home in tiny irregularities in the wall, like the beautiful Lima shells, with the vivid slash of their red mouths.

If these animals form the 'turf' of the cave community, the hydroids are the forests. Though these branching growths resemble plants they are, like their cousins the corals, colonies of individual polyps which attach themselves to each other for mutual benefit. These colonies can extend further out into the flow and so have better access to food than their more sedentary companions on the wall. One of these species of hydroid was discovered to grow to three times its previously recorded length in one of the Andros blue holes. This cave had especially strong currents. Perhaps this had encouraged the hydroid to grow out into the rich flow as much as its structure would allow?

Through these forests and plains move the grazers of the community, measle cowries and mobile crustaceans – shrimps and crabs. The shell of the cowrie is obscured by its dull-grey mantle but when this is withdrawn it is one of the most beautiful inhabitants of the cave.

The shrimps are everywhere! Red eyes reflect the beam of a diver's torch, a cautious, highly-mobile audience for his exploration. Commonest among them are banded coral-shrimps. These colourful red-and-white striped cleaner-shrimps feed on the external parasites of fish. Whether they migrate to the entrance to feed at night or whether they find other meals inside the cave is another of the unanswered questions of the blue holes.

Their first cousins, the lobsters, haunt crevices deep inside, part-time residents of the underworld that may migrate nightly out of the cave to feed, if currents allow. To the exploring diver, they appear as armoured giants, moving in carapaced disdain through their unchallenged domain, the largest of the regular dwellers in the cave.

The deeper into the cave you go, the less frequent life becomes. Corals and anemones are the first to vanish, then the hydroids and the shells. But the sponges, one of the simplest of all animals, manage to exist well into the deep cave. So do the detritivores – the small crustaceans and brown holothurians (sea-cucumbers, all mouth, gut and anus) – that live in the sediment on the floor.

Few of the marine caves so far explored allow man to see much beyond the start of these inner barrens, but on our Conch Sound dives beneath Andros we reached areas over a kilometre from the entrance where very little lived at all. At the end of the cave the walls were bare rock and the few tenacious survivors were pale and fragile sponges, and weak, flaccid ascidians. The environment becomes increasingly cryptic so far in, its new parameters undefined. Eventually there comes a point where only creatures that have fully adapted to a life of total darkness in the extreme conditions of the deep cave, such as the blind cave fish *Lucifuga*, can exist.

Caves like Aquarius, and the Lucayan Caverns, may provide some of the answers to the questions raised by this new deep cave environment. Both have marine connections through entrances in tidal creeks, and both contain in their innermost tunnels a fauna that has adapted more completely than that found in ocean holes.

The exploration of Henford Two was completed the next day. Dennis rolled up in the 'Blue Holes Exploration Vehicle Mark 3'. His customised diving van was a fully-converted cave-diver's mobile H.Q. He brought with him Jeff Bozanic, an American cave-diver, who was on Grand Bahama to study the hydrology of the freshwater lens. Dennis, a great one for napping, immediately went to sleep while we took Jeff on a tourist trip of the Henford Holes. Despite the fierce currents and the size of the entrance passage, Henford Two degenerated, as had so many others, into a maze of small solutional tunnels on three levels. Try as he might, Julian could find no way out of the three-dimensional network and had to return, disappointed, to the surface.

A former NASA engineer with the Apollo programme, and a keen sea-diver, Dennis became fascinated by blue holes while working at a satellite tracking station on Grand Bahama. When the Apollo programme finished, he stayed on, working as a flying instructor and spending much of his spare time exploring underwater caves. His abiding interest was the Lucayan Caverns. Exploration had begun here some years before, when a local diver, Ben Rose, had bravely plunged into the dark water of what was to become Ben's Cave, one of several ways into the Caverns. Over the next decade Dennis and other cave-divers explored a complex maze of tunnels, passing through the halocline again and again as they moved between the freshwater and saltwater layers of the cave. By the time we arrived in 1983, almost ten kilometres of guidelines had been laid in the maze and no fewer than four entrances to the system had been discovered. Three of these were in close proximity, but the fourth was several hundred metres further south in a tidal mangrove creek. Taco Entrance had been connected to Ben's Cave on a long dive by Florida divers Sheck Exley and Gene Melton, and was an important link between the inland cave and the sea.

One of the earliest discoveries was the Skylight Room, a high, domed hall where a tiny hole in the roof led to the surface above, allowing a cool blue light to permeate the chamber. Directly beneath lay a mound of boulders, just below the surface of the water. In the summer of 1973, an American diver, Dr Warren Duncan, discovered a human shin-bone protruding from the pile. Further examination revealed other bones, including part of a human skull. These were sent to the United States for analysis where, owing to the flatness of the cranium, the Smithsonian Institution identified them as Lucayan Indian. The mound produced fragments of several more skeletons and experts decided that it must have been a ritual burial site. If so, it is the only one (so far) of its type to be discovered in the Bahamas. Unfortunately, human greed beat scientific examination to the site. Souvenir hunters, in their ghoulish curiosity, had pulled the mound apart before it could be properly examined.

In 1980, Dennis and his girlfriend, Jill Yager, a biologist who was also a cave-diver, began a study of the life in the cave. For some time they had been aware that they shared the water with small animals, but until then they had paid them little notice, being too entranced with the cave itself. One of the tiny creatures looked like a swimming centipede, blind and white, only a few millimetres long. Here was a primitive creature which resembled a free-swimming type of polychæte worm, but which had characteristics that were more strongly crustacean. The more she studied it, the more excited Jill became, realising that it was something that was completely new to science. She called it *Speleonectes* (cave-swimmer), and established that it was not only a new species of crustacea, but an entirely new genus, family, order and class! She named the class *Remipedia*.

Interestingly enough, *Speleonectes lucayensis* now has a relative, a crustacean known only from fossil remains over 250 million years old, older even than the Bahama Banks themselves. Even more astonishing was Dennis's later discovery of a closer cousin, a second member of the class *Remipedia*, in a flooded lava tunnel in the Canary Islands, several thousand miles away off the North African coast.

An entirely new class of animal is of major significance, and showed that the biology of the caves was not a subject about which to be casual. In 1982 the land above the Caverns was bought by Jack Hayward and given to the Bahamas National Trust as a National Park. Controversy soon erupted! The immense value of the caves as archæological sites had been ruined by human stupidity, and Dennis and Jill were concerned that misuse of the caves themselves might adversely affect the cave environment before it could be properly studied.

The caves were certainly well-dived, not only by cave-divers, but also by commercial organisations which saw them as a tourist resource, to be economically exploited. Not all the divers using the cave had its interests at heart. Serious cave-divers on the island told stories of off-island sports divers being seen leaving the caves with arms full of stalactites. A commercial company making a James Bond movie bulldozed a large part of the National Park overlying the caverns to gain easier access to the entrance. The sheer number of divers entering Ben's Cave each month was severely disrupting the wildlife around the entrance, one of the key biological contact points of the system. In March 1983, the National Trust closed the cave to divers. After a heated Trust meeting in Freeport in June that year, a two-year moratorium was placed on diving in the caverns for other than research purposes, and even for these an official permit had to be obtained. While a policy for future access was being debated, cave-divers had to look elsewhere.

What brought us to East End, in fact, was the search for other caves as scientifically significant as the Lucayan system. With the discovery of the Zodiac Caverns, we were getting closer but there was still too much of a marine influence for true cave life to be able to compete.

That afternoon I took Dennis into Aquarius and down the passage we had first explored to look at the life on the walls and to take photographs. Again we saw *Lucifuga*, the only real cave-adaption discovered so far and, in a side alcove on the way out, a Spiny-cheeked Sleeper. These torpid gobies are another common Caribbean cave fish; Dennis knew them from the Lucayan Caverns and I had seen them in caves in the Dominican Republic, but neither of us had seen one quite so lacking in pigmentation before. It eluded our attempts at capture so we contented ourselves with samples of the filter-feeders on the wall and then made our way out.

Meanwhile, Rob, Julian and Jeff had been in Gemini. Jeff, with his bulky, back-mounted tanks, could not negotiate the low constriction into the main cave, so he and Julian had turned left into a previously unexplored stretch. They discovered a short extension to the entrance series that came to an end at a point too low for them to continue.

Rob was having a more successful time. Tying new line to the end of his old line, he swam only a few metres further before encountering a silt slope, sweeping in on the left of the passage. Following this upwards he saw natural light filtering down from above. He surfaced in the northernmost corner of Lake Two. He had completed the first underwater traverse between one cave entrance and another on Sweeting's Cay. This was a major link in our 'trans-Cay system', and we could now trace an aquatic link from Zodiac Creek, via the small aston collapse of Lake Three, to the main lake in the centre of the island. We were more than half-way to the south side.

Back underwater, Rob set off up a new passage that ran westwards from the second entrance but suddenly found himself involved in an underwater confrontation. The passage was already occupied by an enormous fish, a grouper. An unusual inhabitant so far from the sea, the grouper would have none of Rob's presence. This was its territory! Angrily, agitated by the intrusion, it swam at Rob, butting him with its head. Rob, not wanting to start a fight in the dark cave, and somewhat nonplussed by the turn of events, retired and went to explore elsewhere.

He emerged at his starting point in Lake Three having taken out his frustration on a small amphipod that swam around dizzily in the film container in which it had been caught. More interestingly, Rob had stumbled across a small, scattered area of bones beyond the narrowing of the cave near the first entrance. These, we felt, could have been washed in by exceptionally high tides, congregating in an area of calmer water beyond the constriction. Or perhaps they were the remains of some animal from the far past of the cave? A later analysis of the bones suggested that one might be part of a human cheekbone. If this was so, then they were probably washed in. The depth of the cave at the point Rob found them was well below water when man first arrived in the area.

Next day, Julian and I followed Rob into Gemini and made a photographic run down the chamber. It was one of the most enjoyable cave dives either of us had made, a chance to play tourists through the splendid and mysterious grottoes, and to poke our heads into untouched corners in the hope of finding something new. Rob had gone ahead, carrying a small staging tank to allow him more time at the far end of the cave. This time he was determined not to allow any fish, however big, to interfere with exploration!

He explored a further two hundred metres of passages, emptying his reel in an attempt to find a main continuation in a different direction to the second lake. Two large passages led, at a depth of twenty metres, back towards Hinchliffe Hall in Aquarius, but both came to premature ends in a jumbled chaos of roof collapse. There was no way through to the other cave.

Rob's lights appeared in the distance as we reached the far end of the main hall. There was a brief flurry of excitement on our exit when he produced a small white creature that looked like *Speleonectes*, but it later turned out to be only a free-swimming species of polychæte worm. Gemini, like Aquarius, seemed virtually played out.

In the closing days of the expedition, we turned our

attention to the other side of the Cay, to the caves in the two large lakes behind the settlement. On 9 July we carried our gear through the bush behind the village and explored Lake One. The algal entrances were eerie, a far cry from the bright colours of the ocean holes. Their very aura was enough to arouse concern even before we left the light of day. Anitra Thorhaug, an American expert on algae and seagrasses, was the latest in our string of visitors, and we left her happily studying the flora of the lake while we picked entrances and began to explore.

In less than half an hour, Julian and I were back at the kitting-up site kicking our heels. All our caves had quickly ended in choking banks of silt or broken rock. Rob had again done better. He had chosen the larger of a pair of entrances on the eastern side of the lake and was busy adding Sagittarius to the list of celestially-named caves. While we waited for him I connected his second entrance to the main cave through a low and extremely muddy squeeze that we did not repeat. For some reason we seemed to be moving in an upward scale of grandeur as we explored, as though being rewarded by an increasing revelation of just how much these caves could offer.

The speleothems in Sagittarius were as pure as the day they were formed, as profuse as those in Gemini, but unstained by the centuries of marine accretion. Rob explored most of the cave alone, passing along clear, delicate tunnels to reach a third entrance in the bush behind the village, south of the lake. This was only a couple of hundred metres from the choked blue holes in the southern creek but this entrance, too constricted to climb out of, was the furthest point we reached in our aquatic journey across the Cay.

While Rob was exploring the cave in Lake One, Julian and I moved to the south end of Lake Two, to try to find a system that would link the two main lakes together. With rapidly dwindling time, we hastily explored Virgo, the last of our 1983 discoveries, through two huge branching halls that we saw only faintly in the fading glow from our torches. Our equipment, like ourselves, was beginning to feel the pace. At the top of the chamber closest to Lake One a low passage led off to the south. This was our last chance to connect the two lakes together and I took it, reeling down a wide bedding passage less than half a metre high. While doing so, I became aware that the rock was subtly different here, fresher, brighter, less obscured by sediment. This was a new passage and the floor I was swimming over had, in the not too distant past, been roof. It stretched out in one long, unbroken slab and when, thirty metres in, the cave choked in I was glad to be able to turn round and head out, away from the overwhelming feeling of instability, of being a human sandwich between two hard slices of rock.

So our 1983 expedition came to an end. In a few brief weeks we had explored more than two kilometres of underwater caves beneath the seas and islands of eastern Grand Bahama. We had mapped and examined over eighty entrances, fourteen of which had led us to major caves. The Zodiac Caverns were without doubt our most significant discovery, the remnants of an ancient and complex system beneath the embryonic rocky flats of Sweeting's Cay.

6

Return to the Zodiac

Champagne corks popped and the sound of applause echoed round the dripping walls of the ninth chamber in Wookey Hole. The three divers in the cold sump pool looked embarrassed. The open bottle was passed from hand to hand, its sweet froth trickling into the brown muddy waters of the pool.

'O.K., cut!' said a small, bearded figure, rising from behind a film camera.

It was the autumn of 1982, shortly after the Conch Sound epic, and Martyn Farr, Rob Parker and I had just surfaced after Martyn's record-breaking dive in the deep final sump of Wookey Hole far beneath the Mendip Hills. We had been underground for two days, with Rob and I acting as support to Martyn, who had managed to reach a point 150 metres into the murky waters of the last underwater passage before encountering a low and silt-floored squeeze at a depth of sixty metres. This was deeper than anyone had been in a British sump and was an achievement not only in exploration terms but in the sheer physical effort necessary to get divers and equipment along the difficult passages, above and below water, that led to the end of the cave, over a mile into the bowels of the hill.

Despite the strenuous underground journey that had preceded the dive, everything had gone smoothly. The only upset had been the flooding *en route* of the sealed container that carried our spare film. The dive was being filmed as the climax to a cave-diving episode in a series on high-risk sports, and though the wet film was a disappointment, it did not spoil the dive.

It was not until Martyn had surfaced, after more than an hour's decompression in the mud-filled terminal sump (most of it spent breathing pure oxygen to speed up the process in the bitterly cold water), that things began to go wrong.

While Martyn continued to breathe oxygen on the surface, to accelerate the removal of the nitrogen absorbed in his body, Rob gathered two of the used air tanks and began his dive back to the air filled galleries before the penultimate sump. There, in one of the high-level passages, we had established an overnight camp. Rob's heavy-duty neoprene drysuit, necessary for the long exposure to cold and wet conditions, was leaking and he was beginning to shiver. He wanted to change into dry clothes and brew a hot drink for our return.

Ten minutes later, as I was preparing to follow, his lights reappeared. His news sent a different chill through us – it appeared that the line that connected our chamber to the rest of the cave had broken at a particularly awkward section, where the line was belayed underwater to a large rock. Groping blindly round the obstruction, his numbed fingers had found only loose ends of the cord. Getting increasingly cold, and now worried about his diminishing air supply, he decided to retreat and tell us the worst.

When he had stopped shivering a little, and the water had settled, he tried again. He was back even sooner, certain now that the line had broken. Visibility at the constriction was appalling and he knew that he was wasting both his air and his time in trying any further.

By now we were growing concerned. We were not due out of the cave until the following morning. It would be afternoon before people became worried enough to find divers capable of reaching us, and it would take much longer to get them to the cave and find and repair the broken line. By then, cold and tired as we already were, we would be in very serious trouble.

Rob did not have enough air left for another failed attempt. We decided that I should try next, and while we waited for the sump-water to settle and clear a little, I collected as much loose line as I could from the pieces floating by the belay at the edge of the pool. With fifteen metres or so of scrap line wound round my arm, I hoped that it might be possible to get beyond the boulder and find the other end of the broken line. That was our only chance of getting out.

Half an hour later I began the attempt. By the time I reached the obstructing block I had caught up with the suspended mud that the earlier dives had stirred up. The current had not washed it downstream as fast as I had hoped. Visibility was down to less than a metre. My groping on the line seemed to confirm Rob's fears, for all I could find on the far side of the rock were frayed ends. I tied the end of the scraps on my arm to the belay on the old line, and slid over the rock into the descending continuation. Fifteen metres further on I came to the base of the sump. The flooded section was formed in a long V-shape, 100 metres from air to air, and twenty-six metres deep at its lowest point. This was as far as the scraps of line would reach. With the end gripped in my hand, the line as taut as I dared pull it, I swung like a pendulum from side to side. In the cold brown mists of the muddy sump there was no sign of the downstream guideline. The decompression meter on my arm was edging towards the red – if the dive went on much longer, I too would have to decompress, and my own air supplies were running low. I looped the end of the line around a small rock on the floor at the low point of the sump (at least it took us a little closer to safety) and swam back to the constriction.

I looked at the rock from the other side and immediately realised what had happened. On the downstream side the line had been drawn tightly into a thin crevice in the rock just below the knot. There it had jammed. Approaching from upstream, as Rob had, the continuing line could neither be seen nor felt. Loose ends where the belay had been tied on had fooled both Rob and myself into thinking it had broken. I almost laughed with relief.

There was still a slight dilemma. If I returned to tell the others, I would move into decompression time. I had already broken rules by moving into my reserve thirds on one tank, trying to get through. I couldn't spare the air. The sensible option would be to turn round and complete the dive out and trust that my non-appearance back at the end would suggest that I had got through, and not that something more serious had happened. Moving the line out of the crack so that it floated freely, I turned and swam back down the deep notch of the 'V' and up the slope of coarse sand beyond to surface in the welcome lake in Wookey 24. The first thing I did when I reached the site of the camp was to start the stove and boil water. When the others arrived they would need hot drinks! The water was scarcely warm when Rob appeared, followed ten minutes later by Martyn. He had had his own quiet epic in the sump and had had to drop a set of used tanks he had been carrying through the sump. They were recovered the following day.

Our underground meal was semi-cooked but delicious, washed down by wine that had lain in the cave since the previous attempt on the end five years before. Now pushing beyond the new limit, the deep squeeze, would be a job for the next generation.

By contrast, our journey out the next morning was almost straightforward, despite the zip on my drysuit breaking, and allowing it to flood. The thinsulate under-suit I wore did its work and kept me going until the lights of the show cave shone through the water in the distance. Knowing what the reception was likely to be, I hung back until last, letting Martyn have his glory, and allowing Rob the job of surfacing behind him. The glare of film lights

32 An East End blue hole, surrounded by seagrass beds

33 Lizard, Sweeting's Cay

34 (*opposite left*) A Banded Coral Shrimp on a bed of sponge and bryozoans

35 (*opposite below*) A delicate Arrow-Crab in a blue hole entrance

36 (*right*) Delicate yellow fan-worms filter the inflowing current in a marine blue hole

37 (*below*) A spiny lobster in a crevice, surrounded by hydroids

38 (*top left*) A Measle Cowrie, with its beautiful dappled shell
39 (*top right*) Coral polyps extended to feed in the organic
nourishment of the tidal inflow, deep in a blue hole entrance
40 (*above left*) The waving tentacles and vivid pink mouth of an
Arca shell
41 (*above right*) Delicate anemones in a marine cave

and the cheers of the tourist party lining the catwalk were embarrassing, and both Martyn and Rob looked as though they too wished themselves back underwater.

The small bearded figure came down from behind his camera. 'You know, I think you guys are absolutely bloody insane,' he said.

Leo Dickinson has established himself as an adventure film-maker of international repute. His filming career has involved leaping from balloons over the Sahara (he is an expert skydiver), and taking part in complex, acrobatic aerial manoeuvres with other parachutists high in the skies over California; tramping across the ice deserts of Patagonia and up the snows of Everest. Leo's life seems to have been spent on a search for the ultimate adventure. An accomplished mountaineer, one of his most recent escapades had taken place during the shooting of a solo climb of the Eiger North Wall by Welshman Eric Jones. Recreating an accident from a previous ascent, Leo and two skydiving friends leapt from a helicopter with a stark, mile high North Wall as their backdrop. The cold was intense and they made several attempts before Leo was sure he had the shot he wanted – one of his companions, in period dress, tumbling over and over in the air, parachute disguised as a rucksack. The result on screen is chilling. The difference between a dummy dropping and a human body tumbling is vast. Leo's drive for the ideal shot created a sobering perspective to the climb. Nothing, however, would induce Leo to venture any further into caves, flooded or not, than he had foolishly allowed himself to be propelled in Wookey – or so he thought then.

After our return from Grand Bahama in 1983, there was little talk of another expedition there. I had spent three summers in the Blue Holes and wanted a break. Julian and Rob had their minds on their next project and immediately disappeared to Spain. In the high Picos de Europa they joined a team of cavers in the exploration of a 'dry' system that had been discovered recently. The cave went deep, over 1,000 metres, and both Rob and Julian were on the teams that bottomed the system at a record depth, deeper than any British team had caved before.

By autumn I had finished writing the report of the 1983 expedition and had realised more than ever just how little we had really found out about the caves we had explored in the Bahamas. Our maps told little other than where we had been, though they hinted at clues as to how the caves had formed. What was the reason for the strange, shimmering intermixture we had seen at the end of the expedition in Virgo and Sagittarius, when we swam from one layer of saltwater to another? Did these layers have any effect on the life in the caves? Why were our Zodiac holes so different from the Lucayan Caverns and the Blue Holes we had explored earlier on Andros?

Rob, back working as a carpenter on building sites in Bristol, was keen to go back. Julian came down from Manchester, taking a break from his engineering studies at university, and we talked about the possibility of a return to Sweeting's Cay. The idea of making a film in the caves came up. East End seemed an ideal place for this, with the spectacular ocean holes set against their more enigmatic inland cousins. The exploration of new caves would make an exciting addition to the story.

Making a film introduces new dilemmas. If we were going to tell the world about the caves, we had to make sure we did it in a way that emphasised their seriousness, to point out that blue holes such as these were as inaccessible to the average sports diver as the high peaks of the Himalayas are to a weekend rambler.

When sports divers use caves to exercise machismo tragedy strikes a little too often. The clear inland springs of Florida, less than 100 miles from the Bahamas, are often used as foul weather alternatives to sea-diving. Over the last decade, more than 200 divers have died as a result of men and women breaking the rules and entering the caves beneath the springs without torches, or guidelines, with inadequate air supplies, and without any experience of how to behave underwater with a solid rock roof over their heads. The underground lure is exciting but the game ceases to be an adventure when things go wrong. The Florida statistics are frightening, and we did not want to translate them to our Bahamian caves.

But how do you film in such an environment, in totally dark, fragile underwater caves? Dennis Williams had been involved in making a documentary in the Lucayan Caverns. It had taken him and cameraman Paul Mockler a year to complete it. Anything we could do would have to be done in less than a tenth of that time.

Leo Dickinson had often said that he would try anything in the way of adventure sports, except cave diving. Even watching us disappear into the dark water at Wookey Hole, at the end of the brightly-lit show cave, made his flesh crawl. Slowly, he seemed to be changing his mind. A lecture tour of Australia gave him the chance of trying scuba gear for the first time, and he returned from the balmy waters of the Great Barrier Reef full of confidence that cave diving too might be within his grasp. I decided to call his bluff.

When it finally came to it, persuading Leo that he could dive into a blue hole was not as difficult as we might have expected. Persuading him that he wanted to start the dive from a small aeroplane several hundred metres above the hole was a different matter.

In the anticipated film, I wanted to find a means of portraying a blue hole graphically without a long and complicated explanation. One of the more spectacular ways would be to start from high above the island, where the sea, the land and the blue openings of the caves could be seen far below. Then to move in, in a long shot that went straight for one of the blue holes, breaking the surface and continuing below water, to reveal the cave. A difficult film sequence to obtain, but it would be spectacular.

This was where Leo came in, as the power behind that

long, descending shot. On the telephone, Leo was enthusiastic but wary. I took a copy of George Benjamin's film to show him. Half-way through, he turned and said, in mock seriousness, 'I'm not too sure about this, you know. I don't think I've seen anything on this film yet that doesn't bite!'

With Leo keen on the surface camerawork, we needed to find someone capable of the much more demanding underwater filming. Leo's diving experience was far too limited for him to be able to work inside the caves. Fortunately, we did not have too far to look.

Peter Scoones is, in many way, similar to Leo. His camerawork responds best to challenges and he has worked in virtually every kind of underwater environment imaginable. A tough, bearded character in his mid-forties, he is an idiosyncratic perfectionist who, in his youth, had raced yachts to Olympic standard. A background in technical photography in the R.A.F. and the North Sea underwater industry meant that he is uniquely qualified as both a cameraman and underwater technician. He has an established background in lighting difficult situations underwater and, in 1982, had been our main underwater cameraman on the Conch Sound expedition. He has won more underwater photographic awards than any other cameraman in Britain, and had mentioned previously that he would be interested in working on, as he put it, a 'proper film of underwater caves'.

Slowly the film took shape. Support from the Royal Geographical Society and British Sports Council helped make the task easier, and continuing Royal Patronage from H.R.H. The Duke of Kent lent an added air of respectability to the Zodiac Project. Old and new sponsors offered equipment and logistical support but the film was proving to be a stumbling block. Several companies expressed enthusiasm for it, but none would commit themselves to financial backing, obviously concerned about whether we would, in the final event, be able to deliver the goods.

Return to the Zodiac

With the film still in the balance, I went out to the small Pacific island group of Palau, to join a B.B.C. team from the Natural History Unit. They were making a film on the wildlife of the islands and were keen to include footage of caves.

The Palau Islands are largely limestone, but a limestone that has been uplifted by volcanic action to give a vertical relief of over 200 metres. Caves here have been formed by the action of underground rivers – a more 'traditional' manner than the Bahamian ones. The Palauan caves have also been subject to the glacial rise and fall of the sea, and Palau too has underwater blue holes.

The limestone landscape of Palau is breathtaking. Tall, sharp ridges separate steep-sided valleys, some of which are entirely encircled by the high rock. These enclosed hollows, dolines, mark a centre of underground drainage, where water takes a subterranean route to the sea. The rising level of the ocean since the formation of these hollows means that many of them now contain saltwater lakes, far deeper than their land-locked counterparts on Sweeting's Cay. We dived in one of these lakes, on the island of Eil Malk.

The water was alive with jellyfish, an immense population of pulsating, jostling Medusae. From above, the kilometre long lake resembled a pool in which a million giant frogs had spawned. To swim underwater amid this translucent, enveloping throng was an eerie and exciting experience and one of the most unusual of my diving career.

As in the Bahamas, the lake descended to a sulphurous layer, with cold, clear seawater beneath. The small caves ran off at different corners of the lake, a little below the surface. In one of these, a cave so small that I could only get in by squeezing through the narrow entrance with a single tank pushed ahead of me, I discovered that Palau also had its blind cave fish. Hanging in the water in front of me, in a tiny chamber barely large enough for me to turn around, two white, completely eyeless brotulids floated silently, their eel-like tails rippling gently to counter the slight current. They looked so like the Bahamian *Lucifuga* that it was impossible to tell them apart at a glance. *Lucifuga* had never been recorded outside the Caribbean but here, in a different ocean on the other side of the world, was a close cousin whose ancestors had gone down the same road of adaption that allowed them to inhabit caves. Its dark deep-sea ancestry gave this brotulid a distinct advantage over other fish, and to find it here was an exciting discovery.

With our field dates getting dangerously close, I took the blue holes film to Richard Brock of the B.B.C. Natural History Unit in Bristol. At the time, the unit had a reputation for being wary of natural history films with a human content, and I was a little surprised when Richard became enthusiastic not only about blue hole wildlife, but about Leo's parachute sequence. He wanted an adventure wildlife film that showed how natural history camerawork could move into the most remote environments of earth in pursuit of new animals. Our original fifty-minute film had to be reworked into a thirty-minute budget feature, which created new difficulties, but it gave the venture the final green light.

With the increased natural history content to the film, I was a little concerned at the lack of scientific strength on our team. My own knowledge of blue holes biology was based on field observation rather than scientific background, and was certainly not up to Natural History Unit standards. Dennis and Jill would be unavailable for most of the time. We needed someone with a good general knowledge of marine biology who would be able to cope with working in an underwater cave. Strangely enough, someone with the ideal qualifications had turned up on my doorstep, literally, just before the Palau trip.

Sarah Cunliffe was a young marine biologist who for the past couple of years had been working in diving medicine at an experimental unit at Fort Bovisand in Devon. Having come to see me for an entirely different reason, she ended up in Palau at the same time as I did, and we dived together enough for me to realise that she was not only a good biologist but an extremely capable diver as well. Her medical background was an additional qualification and I had no qualms about asking her to join the team.

Our second scientist, a non-diving one, was Lucy Heath. Lucy had recently returned from a seven-month walking holiday in South America, having left a job as a field geologist with the Soil Survey to do so. She was currently training to teach geology at a college in Bath. I had known her for several years, during which time she had become familiar, albeit at second-hand, with blue holes. She was a keen caver and had an exuberant, bouncy personality. It had been obvious in 1983 that the geology and water chemistry of the caves played a big part in their biological story, and we needed the extra perspective Lucy could give to comprehend fully the blue hole environment.

With Leo's wife, Mandy, and Peter's girlfriend, Georgette Douwma (herself an excellent underwater photographer), as their respective assistants, our team was complete. With nine members, it was a somewhat more ambitious venture than our 1983 expedition.

I flew out a few days ahead of the rest of the team, to make last-minute arrangements in Freeport with the help of Dennis and John Hinchliffe. Jack Rogers had sold the A-frame to his neighbour, John Schlanbusch, and John had offered us this as our base. I had to be sure that we could get everyone and everything there with the minimum of trouble.

A trip out to Haul Over, to check the A-frame and run over details with John (who would be at his family home in Norway during our stay), gave me an impressive scar with which to greet the others. John's two dogs, there to guard the premises when John and his wife Eileen were not about, were good Bahamian bush dogs, with a near-total prejudice for strangers. 'Michelle', the bitch, was all bark and would have fooled no one close up, but the older male,

'Nasty', had not been so-called for nothing. Trusting too much in his memories of me from the year before, I bent down to say hello just a little too quickly. A quick grab at his jaws kept the damage to four canine teethmarks on my left cheek. The rest of the team, stepping off the aeroplane a couple of days later, looked at the scars and wondered what they were letting themselves in for.

We settled into the temporary comfort of the Princess Hotel, guests of the management. The air-conditioned rooms and the casual holiday atmosphere downstairs contrasted sharply with the sandflies, mosquitoes and humid heat of East End and the anticipated afflictions of the coming five weeks!

The sight of a large, open lorry shuddering to a halt outside Freeport's smartest hotel, laden with large wooden boxes and crates of food, caused little stir amongst the tourists inside the building. This was the Bahamas. All the film equipment, repacked after a day of filming Pan Am aircraft landing and the tourist sights of Freeport, was stacked on top. With people and personal baggage making the fourth and fifth layers, the Zodiac Project finally hit the road.

It was a road that degenerated by stages all the way to Drake's Dock, the last accessible pier on the eastern mainland of Grand Bahama. As far as the U.S. Space Tracking Station (the 'missel base') it was good, smoothly-Tarmacked highway. Beyond that it roughened, potholes appeared and we slowed down. Further still, the road changed to dirt-track, with deep water-filled hollows, lending an isolated air to the far end of the island that the sixty-kilometre drive barely justified. By the time the lorry jerked to a halt at the Dock, everyone and everything was well-shaken.

Gear was ferried round to Haul Over in the newly-inflated Zodiac and the small whaler that John Schlanbusch had left with us. The pile that did not make it that evening was left at Deep Water Cay. The new managers of

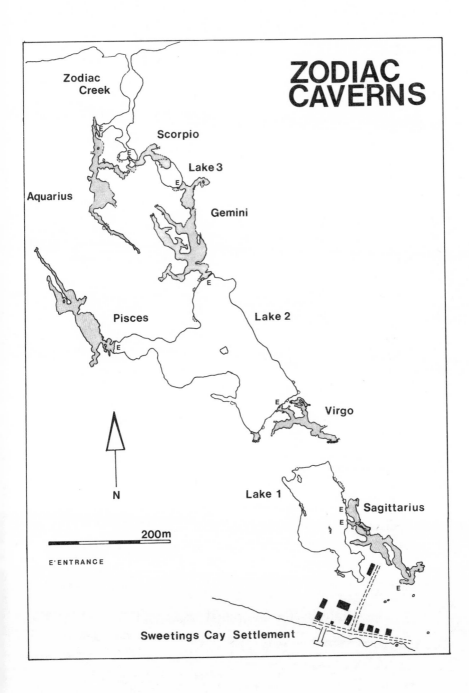

ZODIAC CAVERNS

Zodiac Creek

Scorpio

Lake 3

Aquarius

Gemini

Pisces

Lake 2

Virgo

N

200m

E·ENTRANCE

Lake 1

Sagittarius

Sweetings Cay Settlement

the bone-fishing resort there, John and Mary Brooks, were old friends who were keen to help wherever they could — both were extremely experienced American cave-divers. We had originally hoped to have use of a large air compressor they were having fitted but it had not yet appeared. We would in the meantime have to rely on the small portable Coltri compressor we had brought with us. Compressing air seemed to be the bane of all our blue holes expeditions.

By the end of the first day, 29 June, unforeseen problems were emerging. The major concern was our Zodiac and its engine. I had borrowed a 35 hp Johnson outboard from Colin Rose, of Outboard Services in Freeport, but had not realised that we needed one with a long shaft to cope with the transom height of the Zodiac. Ours had a short shaft; the propellor was barely underwater. Eventually Rob Parker's professional carpentry skills were called upon and a few inches of transom removed. We hoped that Zodiac would not mind the rough customisation of our borrowed boat.

In the late afternoon of the first day, we made a checkout dive to sort out any minor equipment snags and allow people to look at the caves. Rob went off to explore a side passage in Gemini, left from the year before, Julian wanted to examine a new entrance at the far end of Zodiac creek that we had missed last time, and I took Sarah to Aquarius, to show her the fauna of a tidal cave.

That was a mistake on my part. We arrived at an unfortunate time, arriving at the cave just as the current slackened before the start of the inflow, which meant any silt we stirred upon entry would move with us into the cave. This was potentially dangerous, and it brought vividly to mind a recent tragedy that had occurred in the entrance to the cave as we were beginning to plan our return to the island.

Just after New Year in 1984, Jack Rogers and a friend, John Heimer, had gone to dive in the entrance to Aquarius to fish for dinner. Wearing only single tanks they had discovered at the bottom of the entrance shaft just how easy it was to stir the silt on the floor into blinding suspension in the water. Jack had turned, instantly aborting the dive. He was sure that John was following suit immediately behind. After a few minutes on the surface, waiting alone, it was obvious that something was wrong. Jack made an attempt to re-enter the cave, but could see nothing. Returning in desperate haste to Haul Over, he returned with John Schlanbusch and tried again. By that time John Heimer had been in the cave too long to be alive.

It was virtually a carbon copy of the incident in Uncle Charlie's Blue Hole. A diver, not equipped for cave-diving, had become lost in a silt-out only just out of sight of day and failed to emerge alive.

The after effects of the tragedy at New Year compounded our own problems. There was no sign of the guideline I had laid through the widest section of the shaft and I had to lay a new line in, rediscovering the route. By the time we reached the base of the shaft, fifteen metres down, our visibility was down to less than half a metre. Sarah was having difficulties with her lights: her main unit (a waist-mounted German lamp similar to the American design) had not been fully-charged and would not work. She changed to one of her smaller back-up torches but it took us only a metre or two more to realise that conditions were atrocious; it was far too dangerous for her to continue. With a brief look at what we could see of the vestibule fauna, we groped our way back out.

Sarah, taking her mask off in the open air, looked a little shaken. The conditions had been excessively severe for an inexperienced cave-diver; we had entered the cave at the worst possible time and she had, on this occasion, entirely misplaced her trust in me. I was mortified. I had been too sure of her ability and had let her down. It was not an auspicious start to our work and, to cover my shame, I went back into the cave alone to sort out the mess made of the lines by the recovery of John Heimer's body. What I found made me even happier that we had aborted the dive when we did. Just beyond our turning point I came across the original line in an enormous tangled mess, together with thin coils of line left by the rescue divers. Moving carefully, I bundled them together and stuffed them in an alcove to one side while I swam further into the cave to check the condition of the lines there.

Moving fast, to stay ahead of the murky water, I swam past the large column that had ended my first dive in the cave and down into the deeper, clear passage we had then explored. Orange flatworms writhing on the floor and delicate Arca shells were new to me, unseen the year before. The latter lay loosely embedded in the mud, with fine, waving tentacles emerging from subtly-coloured pink lips.

The lines beyond the entrance area looked in fine condition. I swam back out, removing the old coils on the way. I was still angry with myself, upset at my naïve over-enthusiasm, and hoping that I had not destroyed Sarah's faith in me.

Small logistical problems seemed to fill the first few days. By the end of the week I was tired, argumentative and weary, feeling that people were too often coming to me with queries they could more easily, and more efficiently, sort out on their own. Often my answers were wrong, which served only to exacerbate my own and their irritation.

The psychology of expeditions would make a fascinating study. Here we had a bunch of assorted, highly-motivated individuals together in close contact for five weeks, sharing a two-room house, each with a slightly different reason for being there. I for one found it difficult; my own preference would be for small, three or four man expeditions, where each participant knows the others before the field stage, and has a well-defined sphere of responsibility. I am not a great leader, usually becoming preoccupied with the project I am involved in rather than the minor trials and tribulations of those around me. I expect people to adapt more readily to expedition conditions and responsibilities than they often do. Nor, unfortunately, am I insensitive to petty criticism; one of the more essential qualities of leadership is a thicker skin than mine.

A division opened between Peter Scoones and myself early on in the trip. Peter never really understood the presence of Lucy and Sarah on what he regarded primarily as a filming venture. I found it difficult to get across that we were in reality a filming *expedition*, where we needed to continue to amass hard data on the subjects we were filming, in order to understand them more completely. Despite the first serious blue hole explorations being made over twenty years ago, there are still no real experts on the caves, and our film needed to include serious scientific work to complement fully the visual imagery. We hadn't yet established anyway all the film's content. I did not want to find myself going elsewhere at the end of the expedition in order to film *Remipedia*. Though our film was to be centred on the Zodiac Caverns, and the caves immediately around them, there had been no sign of the 'Little Crittur', as Dennis and Jill called it. An early priority was a search for the tiny crustacean in the caves of Sweeting's Cay.

There were three possibilities. One, and the most hopeful, was that we had simply missed it in 1983. It takes a new skill to shorten one's focus of attention to the metre or so in front of one's eyes in a clear underwater cave, where visual boundaries are so well-defined a few metres further on. This self-induced myopia is difficult enough in open air. Try focusing on a point one metre in front of your eyes, estimating the distance by guesswork. Then place a finger there to see if you were right. Difficult? Now try it in the dark. We could easily have missed *Remipedia* in 1983.

The second possibility was that we might find it in one of the unexplored caves in Lake Two, those furthest from the influence of the sea. There were several unvisited entrances, the largest of which lay at the end of a channel running off the western side of the lake.

The third possibility was that it might not be here at all, because of the evident lack of a freshwater lens. Though *Remipedia* are salt-water creatures, all the sites in which, so far, they have been found had a freshwater lens above. It was felt that *Remipedia* might move between the layers to feed, and that a distinct lens might be a prerequisite for the animal. I felt that the entrance we had seen from the air further inland might be a better possibility.

But before the hunt could begin there were other priorities, one of which was deciding in which caves to concentrate the filming. Peter had produced a lighting system that he felt would solve any question of illumination. Three 1,000 watt filming lamps would be placed in the chosen caves, linked by thick, waterproof cables to a 3,800 watt Honda generator on the surface. The extra wattage was necessary to counter the voltage drop over the length of cable it would take to get the lights in the caves and still allow enough surplus wire to position them to best effect.

Virgo was our first choice. Despite a short constriction in the entrance shaft, the cave was roomy and well-decorated, and putting the lights in place would not be too difficult. Peter made a reconnaissance dive with Julian, and came back delighted with the place.

The haul to get the equipment in was less exciting. Two hundred metres of cable, attached to three large lamps, made a cumbersome load. Enlisting the help of several startled Bahamians from the village, we staggered through the bush with the lighting gear and diving equipment over the half-kilometre or so to the Virgo entrance. Leo Dickinson had already decided that his place was to film us sweating through the undergrowth, so we covered the distance in short bursts while Leo leapfrogged in front.

A comic-book sequence took place when Leo unwittingly placed himself directly on the track and so, for the sake of continuity, we bent our course and dutifully filed past, doing our best to look tough and exhausted, straight into the impenetrable scrub at the side. Leo was oblivious. He finished filming the last person, turned, and looked at the crushed-up bunch piled cheek-by-jowl behind him in the thorns.

'Lost the path?' he said, innocently.

We made a short filming dive that day, using Peter's mobile 250 and 500 watt underwater lamps. It was Sarah's first dive into one of the inland caves since the abortive attempt in Aquarius and I hoped that it would go better this time. I was glad of the powerful lights we carried; caves seem so much less frightening when the darkness is effectively banished.

I ran a new line in to meet the old and we all passed the constriction with ease. The big lights were turned on at the base of the shaft. The effect was breathtaking. In 1983 I had explored this cave with a single, small torch, my others held in reserve because the batteries were almost spent. Now almost 800 watts lit Virgo and, like the others, I felt that I was seeing the cave for the first time. Our entrance to the cavern itself, from the base of the shaft, was along a fretted, oval passage, with scalloped sand carpeting the floor. Finning over this, we emerged in a hallway, with passages leading off in three directions. We rose up to the right, into a chamber I had entered on my first dive there the year before, a sloping hall dominated by a magnificent fluted column of flowstone in the centre, half-way up the slope. On the walls on either side, small alcoves held miniature grottoes of stalactites and a surrounding army of columns paid homage to the colossus in their midst.

Peter wrapped his legs firmly around a rock pillar on the floor of the chamber and began filming. Sarah and I moved round the hall, photographing speleothems and looking as scientific as we could. Serpulid worms moved quickly back into their tubes as we approached, obviously extremely sensitive to pressure waves in the water. They reacted to bright lights in the same way; the big filming lamps simply drove them indoors, much to Peter's chagrin, though I found that, with care, I could creep up very slowly with my Nikonos camera and flash off a single shot before they jerked inside.

We spent half an hour exploring the corners of the chamber, with Peter and Georgie moving behind us, filming when they felt that conditions were right. At last Peter's film ran out and he signalled his intention to head for the entrance. As we broke surface and gasped in fresh air, Leo asked Sarah how she felt.

'Before I went down there, I thought this bunch were completely mad.' A grin spread over her face. 'After that, I know why they get so excited about these caves. That was one of the most amazing experiences I have ever had!'

42 The A-frame, with 'Nasty' in charge

43 Morning in the A-frame...an overcrowded dormitory!

44 (*opposite above*) Rob Palmer, Sarah Cunliffe and Peter Scoones prepare to film in Virgo

45 (*opposite left*) Lucy Heath floats in front of a thin 'curtain' of stalactites in Virgo

46 (*above*) The algal-draped entrance to Virgo, Lake Two

47 (*right*) Sarah Cunliffe and Peter Scoones surface from a filming dive to Virgo

48 Intermixing waters soften the focus in the Red Room in Virgo

7

Creatures of Perpetual Night

The filming in the cave was over for the day; exploration could begin. Lake Two had another entrance, unexplored in 1983, at the end of the long western branch. Peter was happily ensconced filming the flora and fauna of the lake, Sarah was collecting it, and I was, for the moment, left to my own devices. Telling Lucy, a little tongue in cheek, that I would only be gone for half an hour or so, I finned off across the warm waters, sweating slightly under the burden of equipment.

The swim took longer than I anticipated. The entrance was only 300 metres away, but I was far from streamlined and the swim was slow. The final stretch down the channel was extremely shallow and at times I had to stagger to my feet and wade. Out of the water, the gear I was carrying weighed over forty kilos, most of it slung uncomfortably around my waist. Wading was indescribably worse than swimming.

At last the entrance appeared, a half-moon crescent, with mangroves curling in on either side and a clear patch of rock immediately above. Rippling algae on the lip of the dark pit betrayed a slight outward flow, too gentle to be discerned otherwise but a promising sign. A tiny knobble of rock on the lip made a solid enough belay for the line, and I pressed the button that vented the air from my jacket and gladly left the hot and sticky afternoon behind.

The entrance was constricted. A tight, feet-first squeeze led down the side of the aston collapse into a low and muddy passage, ten metres down. Grey sponges and twisting, erratic serpulid tubes lined the walls with a pallid coat. Colours were scarce. On the floor, in a flash of pink, a group of Barbouria shrimps scattered as I moved in closer. A common sight in Caribbean caves, these prawns had been spotted in other of the Zodiac Caverns and seemed to be resident here in unusual profusion. Was this a good sign too?

The thin American line was wound round a rock on the floor at the base of the shaft and I moved out into the lower chamber.

A few desultory formations rose out of the mud, reaching upwards towards the brown roof. Hugging the left-hand wall, I spun the line carefully out, conscious of the fine sediment that, with an incautious move, would hide any way out of the chamber behind a cloud of silt.

Peering round a corner, the first thing I saw, suspended in the dark water, was *Lucifuga*, its white, eel-like tail rippling gently in the open cave. Fortunate for me, but not for poor *Lucifuga*. Making a natural history film inevitably involves a 'rape and pillage' philosophy in severe environments such as these, and Peter had asked that anything interesting should be immediately caught, left in the cave if possible, or brought out if not. I immediately caught the fish.

Catching blind animals in underwater caves is not quite as easy as it might seem. They are entirely dependent on an ability to sense pressure waves in the water, using this sense for both hunting and self-protection. For a hulking cave-diver to sneak up on them without their knowing is virtually impossible. I probably created the biggest pressure waves the poor creature had ever known. The trick is to confuse it, to manoeuvre a container of some sort – a plastic bag, a glass jar, nothing necessarily sophisticated – in front of them, while making pressure waves from behind. Generally the ruse fails the first time, the creature senses the impending enclosure, so it has to be chased round the cave until it swims into the bag in desperation for somewhere to hide. The poor *Lucifuga* here was too easy to catch. Once safely in the bag, I could see it had a damaged fin and a very empty stomach. It looked old and starved and I consoled myself with the knowledge that it would have had little future in the cave. Mentally, I named the cave Pisces in its honour.

Holding the fish in the bag like some childhood fairground prize, I turned the corner out of the muddied chamber and into a clear breakdown passage, partially blocked with boulders. Worming my way carefully between the blocks, one-handedly belaying the line here and there, I squeezed into a final chamber only two metres in diameter. At a depth of twenty-one metres in the cold, clear underlayer of deep saltwater, *Lucifuga* and I shared the cave with something else.

Hovering in front of my mask, legs moving in sinuous rhythm, was what looked like a tiny white centipede. I could feel my pulse quicken. Extremely gently, I manoeuvred another plastic bag out of a pocket and, even more gently, herded the little creature into it with a cupped hand. It was too easy. I shut the bag on *Remipedia*, our first from the Zodiac Caverns, and watched it as it suddenly realised its predicament and made a frenzied attempt to escape. Guilt and pleasure tore me in different directions.

I do not like collecting wildlife from caves. I subscribe to the philosophy that any creature, of whatever size, has a basic right to live as long as it possibly can. The law of the jungle is fine, I have no objection to killing for food, or eating meat, but simply to remove a creature that might well be exceedingly rare for the purpose of scientific identification always triggers a guilt complex. It is surely far better to photograph it *in situ*, establish roughly what it is, and then what the population is, and to come back and get specimens later if there is a need. Scientists are more apt to work on a 'bird in the hand' principle. Reluctantly I acquiesce. In an environment that draws and excites me so much, such collection is an act of rape each time. Eventually the hunt itself takes on an atavistic delight of its own, despite the size difference, and impulse drowns concern for life. The caves deserve better from us.

So I found myself in a small chamber with two creatures in plastic bags, trying to escape. These took up one hand and both eyes. In the other hand was a reel and line with a mind of its own, which did not want to be cut and tied off. The tunnel was a dead-end, a false lead, I realised, but I could do nothing about it then. Besides, I had already been longer than I promised and the others would be getting concerned. I left the line down the newly-discovered cave, and returned to shore, deflecting comments on the time by the presentation of my imprisoned pets. The evening was Peter's. With fish tanks, small glass squares and rubber 'O' rings, he created a miniature studio in the A-frame, and captured *Lucifuga* on film.

Unfortunately, that *Remipede* did not make celluloid. Sarah, carefully trying to move it from one container to another, suffered a biologist's nightmare. Her normally steady fingers slipped, and the poor blind crustacean returned to an instant world of underground darkness – down the plughole of the sink!

That meant a second visit to Pisces. Where there was one, there had to be more. So we prayed. In the four years since its discovery in the Lucayan Caverns, the creature had been seen only fifteen times on the island. We sincerely hoped that the Pisces population was more prolific!

Two days later, while Rob and Julian were placing the cable and film lights in Virgo, I returned to Pisces on a *Remipedia* hunt. Back in the bouldery rift at the end of the line, I peered into corners in the hope of catching a glimpse of something white. Within a couple of minutes I had chased a tiny *Remipede* out of hiding and into the framer of my camera's close-up lens. Blinding it with the flash was too much. As I set the camera aside on a rock, the tiny creature sped away.

I began to curse into my regulator (a rather frustrating exercise underwater) but stopped in amazement as a larger *Remipede* swam into view. Perhaps the tiny one had gone to get big brother; this was three times the size, over two centimetres long! Without further ado I went for it. A frantic chase ensued. An animal with a brain at the top of the evolutionary tree went for one with a brain somewhere near the bottom. It was playing at home though, and very nearly escaped. Like its cousin before, it too became a prisoner in a plastic bag, which for good measure went inside a glass jar with the lid screwed firmly down. I paused to catch my breath. *Remipedia*, without a doubt, was the fastest cave-adapted creature of its size I had ever come across.

The silt settled, and I looked around me. Between two boulders above my head, I could peer into a dark void. With new line tied on, I tried to squeeze through. Too tight. I examined the smallish boulder that blocked my way, and then the huge block that balanced above it. It did not take much imagination to see what would happen if I tugged the small one out. Diver sandwich.

Leaving the camera and jar at the line junction, I backtracked up and around, over the large block and into utter darkness. I hung above a rock floor covered with a light scattering of dust. This sloped up on my left out of range of my torches. As my eyes grew accustomed to the sudden change, I dimly made out a roof, and a forest of white columns at the top of the slope. I swam towards them, looking for a wall to follow. There was one but I soon lost sight of it again. I was finning into absolute darkness, in total disorientation, growing more agoraphobic by the second. Night stretched on either side and though the roof was only two metres from the floor there appeared to be nothing holding it up. The white columns had been an isolated group, all that grew here were a few small, stumpy stalagmites, underneath equally small dripstones above. I was scared, wondering just how stable the roof really was. I looked at my depth gauge – nine metres.

I looked at the floor – a mass of broken slabs, that once had been roof. My finning and breathing took on a delicate touch. When at length a wall came into view, I clung to it like a leech.

With the world taking on boundaries again, I took a greater interest in the cave. The present chamber was obviously the result of a massive roof collapse into an older cavern below. At nine metres it was at a higher level, by ten metres, than the main Zodiac system. I could peer down a crevice in the wall to the remnants of the deeper level and look at the shattered remains of stalagmites from a previous era. Glancing around the rocks of the chamber, I grew a little more reassured; the most recent rockfall apparently pre-dated the last sea-level rise. Even the freshest-looking breakdown had small formations growing on top that could not have formed below water. Here was a vivid example of how the lakes had formed. If this chamber collapsed any further, it would be open to the sky, becoming just an extension of the western channel of Lake Two.

There was little sediment on the floor, compared with the other caves. The slow filtration that piled silt in the deeper chambers of Aquarius and Gemini must come from tidal currents. Twice, as I moved down the cave, I came to the tiny skeletal remains of crabs, one relatively recent, its shell still retaining colour, the other far older, from a past age, its very carapace crumbling to dust in the gentle currents of the cave. A small goby, a 'sleeper', peered at me from above a fallen block. I made a mental note to collect it on the way back, if it was there, and passed on, reeling the line across the cave. Deeper in, I continued to find signs of current flow: suspension feeders, dependent on the water movement to bring food along, were scattered sparsely throughout the chamber; long, pale sponges, with enlarged *oscula* to enable them to pass as much water as possible through their central feeding cavity, hung from the roof and walls out into the cave; and the now-familiar serpulid tubes ran their crazy course across rocks, some were old, semi-fossil remains from the past, others were still searching, with fine pink sprays of delicate feelers at the end of their calcareous tubes. One pair, entwined like calcite dancers, grew out from the roof for almost a full metre into the passage below. At the end of each tube, the fan-like appendages moved daintily in the water, fragile feathers at the end of a ridiculously long tube that could not exist in the surface world. The complete absence of serpulid predators this far into the cave, together with the almost imperceptible currents, produced natural curiosities as beautiful as they were unusual.

My line gave out just as a second wall came into view. The chamber appeared to end as the cave sloped away to greater depth. A convenient rock, 175 metres from the entrance, provided the final belay.

Decompressing after the ninety-minute dive, I photographed the flora and fauna of the daylight zone. Looking up a tiny tube just inside the cave, my light reflected from a mirror-like surface that could only be a halocline. It seemed that the cave did lie under a lens, but a shallow one, barely a metre thick.

That evening we spent a long time photographing the captured crustacean before Sarah gave it a fast and merciful death in formalin, well away from the sink. With Leo holding the flash, I had taken what I thought was a whole reel of film before discovering that my camera was empty, and the creature gone. It was obviously my turn for idiocy that night.

Gradually an overall picture of the Zodiac Caverns was emerging. Even in Bahamian terms, the environment here was unusually complex. Within one small patch of island, a complicated inter-relationship existed between caves that were essentially marine, caves that were virtually isolated inland, the curious saline lakes and the island above.

Perhaps before, but more probably after, the sea level first fell at the beginning of the last ice epoch – the beginning of the ice age cycles – the surface of proto-Grand Bahama, exposed for the first time in millennia, dried out and began to crack. The rock, formed largely of unconsolidated, wet oolites (limey muds that had come out of solution in the warm shallow water), shrank as the moisture within drained away or evaporated. Major fractures developed along the edge of the land mass where the sheer weight of the rock encouraged it to slump sideways towards the deep oceanic trench surrounding the Bahama plateau. Other fractures in the drying rock developed at sharp angles to these, weakening the structure still further where they crossed.

A major fracture zone ran parallel to the south shore of Grand Bahama, about a kilometre inshore of the drop-off, through what was to become Sweeting's Cay.

Rain falling on the newly-exposed island collected beneath the surface in the first freshwater lens. Excess water drained to the sea through the fissures and fractures of the porous limestone. In time such routes began to enlarge into small caves. But the main area of cave formation was along the base of the freshwater lens.

The limestone beneath the island lies in perfectly horizontal layers. Other than the pressure of rainwater, there was little to encourage sideways movement of the water as it sank through the exposed rock, little to channel it into regular watercourses. The fractures and fissures provided some escape but in the early Bahamas there were no hills, no valleys, only a few unconsolidated windblown dunes of soft oolitic sand.

In the ponded water of the lens, the water dissolved the surrounding limestone until it became absolutely saturated with minerals. Below the lens, in the deep saltwater zone that permeated the base of the Bahama plateau, the water was just as saturated as the lens.

Where two such saturated waters meet and mix, a third, not-quite-saturated layer forms. This curious natural law meant that the zone of intermixture, the halocline, was a region where more limestone could be dissolved. Gentle tidal movements along the base of the halocline continually removed saturated water and allowed the process to continue. So much rock was removed that caves began to form.

The caves that developed along the halocline in the Bahamas were horizontal caves, hollowing out the rock along distinct layers beneath the island surface. Where there were existing weaknesses – the vertical fissures – cave formation was encouraged and soon an interlinking network of low horizontal caverns joined the larger fissure systems together.

Beneath Sweeting's Cay, a major series of north-south fractures ran close to each other, and between them the Zodiac Caverns formed. Other east-west fissures crossed these, causing a weakness in the rock structure. The base of the lens would appear to have been somewhere between twenty and thirty metres below the surface of the island when this happened, meaning that sea-level was only ten metres or so below its present level when the Caverns formed, if that. In such circumstances the creeks of eastern Grand Bahama would disappear altogether and the island would grow greatly in extent, linking up with nearby Abaco to form one large land mass, capable of supporting a far larger freshwater lens than exists today.

Sea-levels fell again from this 'still-stand', this stable pause. The rock dried out further when the waters that supported the cavern roofs disappeared. As the fractures expanded, so the first rockfalls occurred, then continued with increasing frequency. The period of aston collapse began. Bounded by the vertical fissures that criss-crossed the area, the Zodiac Caverns gradually became separated as whole chambers collapsed, creating the hollows that were to become eventually Lakes One, Two and Three.

Many of the original caverns now lay beneath tons of rock, and the passages that remained were filled with air. The only water to reach these dark tunnels were the innumerable drops of rainwater that trickled down through fissures in the limestone above. Dripstones began to form, the first of the stalagmites and stalactites that would eventually provide the caves with a pristine crystal grace.

There have been several ice ages within the last glacial cycle and it is possible that the caves have gone through several periods of drowning and exposure. Later collapse took with it some of the stalagmites, leaving columns suspended crazily from the roof, or pillars bent at strange angles to the floor. As the sea finally rose to its present level, the caves must for a time have held freshwater lakes, and the halocline must have passed one last time through the caverns, dissolving rock again, before surrendering the caves to the water of the sea.

The shallow chambers of Pisces, Aquarius and Gemini are all areas where the caves have been migrating towards the surface by aston collapse and it is only in a very few places, in the deeper rift passages of Aquarius and Sagittarius, and in similar passages in the other caves, that the original bedrock of the caves can be seen. These passages, and the calcite cores of the dripstones (which can be roughly dated by using sophisticated radio-isotope techniques), may hold the key to the full history of the caves.

If the geology of the caves is beginning to make sense to us, their biology remains elusive.

Aquarius and Gemini, with more direct links with the sea, contain a complex but relatively poorly-established fauna. Many of their inhabitants are trogloxenes, cave-visitors, which would be equally, if nor more, at home on the outside reef. Few are capable of a full life-cycle within the caves save the fan-worms and some of the sponges. Most of the cave fauna has planktonic origins, swept in on the currents, or entering the cave in an adult stage, seeking shelter from the predators of the outside world. *Lucifuga*, high up in the cave food-chain, is the only clear cave-adaptation, efficient enough to compete for food and space with opposition from the world outside the caves.

Pisces is a curiously in-between cave. Its currents come through micro-fissures in the rock; there appears to be no open link with the sea. Its contact point with the outside world is its entrance in Lake Two. Its internal biology reflects this. The lack of marine competition – which finds conditions in the lakes much less acceptable than in the mangrove creeks – means that other life-forms take a more subtle control of the cave ecosystem.

The twisting tubes of fan-worms grow in greater profusion and more complex forms. *Lucifuga*, the blind cavefish, is seen more frequently, and other fully-adapted cave animals, like *Remipedia*, make an appearance. There are tiny crustaceans that share the blind and pigmentless characteristics of *Remipedia* but which feed largely on organic debris – bits of plant matter and the like – that trickle down with rainwater through the thin soils above. The most populous area in all the inland caves is still the twilight zone of the entrance, where sunlight and rich algal growth combine to provide a richer and more sheltered environment than either deep cave or surface lake.

The lakes are worth an expedition of their own. Rarely more than a metre or two deep, they have unusually sheer sides, and a bottom that is virtually flat, with an occasional pit or hollow where the floor has collapsed into a void below. In a few of these small crevices there is still some water flow, and at certain stages of the tidal cycle its presence can be felt as well as seen, by a local cooling of the normally warm and soupy waters.

Algae covers everything, festooning sides, rocks and fallen branches in a wraith-like coat of the palest yellow and green. The primitive plants flourish in the bright sunlight of the shallow, warm waters. In between the longer hanging fronds, smaller bush-like forms and the tiny stalked bowls of 'mermaid's cups' grow in clustered profusion on the shelly limestone floor of the lakes. Where the floor dips into hollows, the colours change subtly to darker, eldritch hues, in a spidery landscape more eerie than the pale shadows above. In the deeper cave mouths, the soft greens turn to brown as the light dims.

In and around the algae, sheltering in it, feeding on it, swimming over and within, a host of other animals dwells in the green bacterial bloom of the lake waters. Cassiopeia jellyfish pulsate on the bottom and within their inverted tentacles symbiotic algae called *zooxanthellae* live. These tiny plant cells consume the waste products of their Medusae hosts, and in an emergency, provide them with an extra source of energy. Small box-jellyfish swarm in delicate shoals near the surface, a myriad transparent population with long and lacy tentacles and small cuboid heads, virtually invisible in the green translucence of the lake.

Crawling across this algal forest, the tiny snails are grazing herds that eventually add their spiral shells to the fragile calcareous dust that covers the lake floor beneath the soft algae. The empty shells are so fine, and so light, that the gentle cave currents can carry them long distances inside the caves. We would occasionally come across small piles of them, deposited by eddies in the flow.

The fish of the lakes seem almost a little out of place in the lilliputian community of lake-dwellers. Mangrove snappers and mosquito fish are to be expected, but the five barracuda that haunt the entrances in Lake Two are high-level predators which it is unusual to find in such an enclosed environment. Either there is an open, linking surface channel to the sea, through some unexplored tangle of mangroves, or the flood-tides of some tempest has brought these grim-looking fish across the island to the lake.

The locals tell stories of large grouper, another marine fish, that lurk in the lake entrance of Gemini, bringing memories of 1983 and the large fish that physically rebuffed Rob Parker's explorations in the cave.

The lakes are an alien world at sunset. As the light dims, the water cools, and the process of photosynthesis slows. The algae vent long streams of oxygen, clear bubbles that rise swiftly to the surface in a million silver trails of gas to link algae and atmosphere in shining streams of light.

After two weeks of dry, hot days, when we watched our freshwater reserves dwindling with a disturbing rapidity, it finally rained. People who, a few minutes before had been gasping in the sapping heat, and driven half-crazy by the itching bites of sandflies, rushed out to stand semi-naked on the dock, letting the cool drops wash the sweat and grime from their bodies. The storm was a blessing. In an hour it filled our water tank and relieved us of the strident, echoing appeals of the resident frog population.

It rained for long enough for us to put off the afternoon's plan for a deep dive in a new cave in Big Creek. This exploration needed exact timing to cope with the fierce reversing tides, and neither Rob nor Julian was keen on braving the seas with a metal-filled boat in an electric storm.

Instead, Rob and Sarah went off to Sagittarius, and Julian and I returned to Pisces to explore the far end of the cave. We left Haul Over late in the afternoon, riding the inflatable round to Zodiac Creek. The gear was carried across to the lake through the tangled scrub above Gemini and we kitted up above the second entrance to the cave.

Trouble started immediately we entered the lake. An 'O' ring blew on my contents gauge, and air streamed out. I had to haul myself out of the water again, de-kit, and dismantle the hose to repair the leak. Julian waited patiently in the water, checking his own gear.

On the journey across the lake, the exhaust valve on my buoyancy jacket trickled air slowly but noisily. This seemed to stop when I swam horizontally, relieving the pressure, so I ignored it.

Then, as I followed Julian down into the cave, one of my regulators suddenly streamed air from a high-pressure leak where it met the valve on the air tank. Grabbing at the tank, I fumbled with the clamp, turning the valve off underwater, purging the regulator and wriggling the valve on its 'O' ring seating. I turned the clamp as tightly as I could and turned on the valve again. The leak stopped.

I became apprehensive. Were these mishaps some sort of warning? Hoping there was truth in the adage that accidents happen in threes, I pressed on, down through Julian's silt-clouds, to catch him up. We met at the bottom of the slope in the big chamber. I wound on the film in my Nikonos and switched on the flash. Julian pushed a bulb into the reflector of the slave-flash he carried and we moved through the water to the columns at the top of the slope.

Ideally I prefer to photograph caves with at least two flashes, to add perspective to the pictures. Julian carried a bulb slave-unit that Rod Beaumont had designed for us on the 1982 Andros Expedition, and which allowed an even spread of light to the cave in front of him. The slave itself was mounted on his helmet, linked unobtrusively by a cable to a small hand-held reflector, allowing it to be placed or pointed in any direction while remaining out of view of the camera. He wore bulbs on a bandolier around his wrist and could change them quickly after each flash.

I fired off three shots before I realised that I had forgotten to attach the small magnet that switched on the slave. An irritating and slightly comic sketch ensued. I swam over to Julian, wrapped an elastic band around the slave to hold the magnet in place, and took the magnet out of my pocket. Immediately I dropped it in the silt. I went down and fumbled around, found it, and came back up. Then I dropped the elastic band . . .

I gave up in disgust and, snapping off one-flash shots, we moved down the cave, photographing relevant geology and wildlife. At the end of the line we parted, Julian to swim back and search for side tunnels while I dumped the camera by the belay, and pressed on into the continuation of the main cave.

New line wound out from the reel and I swam into changed scenery. The passage plunged down into clear phreatic rifts, where flowstone crept across corroded white rock. The needle of my depth gauge crept round the scale. Pits in the floor plunged below thirty metres in depth. At the end the passage broke up into cross-rifts, too small to pursue. *Remipedia* swam there, and a tiny white amphipod scurried over the rock wall to a sheltering pocket. The cave was rich with life.

I backed out, surveying along the line, sinking into one or two of the clear blue pits in the floor of the narrow rift. The rock in this section was fretted, highly-dissolved and very friable. It looked like a farmhouse cheese that had been broken in two by hand, soft, rounded, crumbling.

The camera appeared before me, by the knot on the rock. A pleasant exploration of the second chamber ensued. Another *Remipede*, a different species, and two other white crustaceans went into bags (though the latter managed to escape on the way out), together with a solitary fan-worm and the little rock it grew upon. Despite the unsettling mishaps with equipment on the way in, I felt curiously relaxed, often swimming well off the line, though always aware of its precise position. I was becoming attuned to the dimensions of the cave, comfortable in its surroundings. I passed Julian's exploratory line, tied off on a stalagmite a few centimetres off the main route and I squirmed back through the entrance series to meet him just after his own arrival at the ten-metre decompression stop. He immediately grabbed my arm, and wrote urgently on my slate, 'I've lost my decompression tables!'

Had he been alone, this could have been a potentially lethal mistake. We had both been underwater for an hour and a half; we were well beyond our 'no-stop' time. We *needed* to decompress. I reached casually down for my own tables. The jinx of this dive was compounded. Mine had gone too, lost somewhere back in the boulders at the far end of the cave. I remembered becoming snagged at one point, and swore at my stupidity. It was not at all funny but I could not rid myself of my complacency: 'Very interesting,' I wrote in reply, 'so have I. How much do you trust decompression meters?'

The automatic meter on my arm was well into the red, but we tended to rely on these more as a back-up, preferring to compute our own decompression for each dive. Julian did not react for a moment but then a resigned look of wry amusement came over him. He took his regulator out and gave a funereal grin. Auspiciously, we had both made virtually identical dives the day before, each almost uncannily paralleling both the time and depth of the dive today. We repeated our times, adding extra minutes for safety, and surfaced at 8.30, as the last pale glow of twilight faded. We swam moodily back across the dark lake, each praying our calculations had been sufficient.

As we lifted our heads from the water, the noise hit us. The high whines of errant mosquitoes blended into the over-powering hum of supporting aerial hunters. Hurriedly stuffing gear into bags, we tried to stagger back to the boat with our tanks on, stumbling and tripping over the broken rock beneath our feet, caught at by thorns and vines in the darkness. I kept both mask and helmet on but could feel my skin crawling with insects. It became an exhausted rout. My bag was abandoned to be recovered in the morning. We staggered through the mangroves by the creek like actors in a Hitchcock horror film, to collapse in the water and drown the blood-sucking insects.

The episode had taken far too long – the hauling of the gear, the problems with equipment, the dive itself and the nightmare return journey through the thorns. We reached the A-frame at 10 o'clock, just as a rescue party was about to set off in search of us.

As we sank down in front of the coffee pot, Leo remarked facetiously that they had imagined Julian pinned to the wall by a giant female *Remipede* while two others pushed me down the plughole of a speleo-sink. Sarah, while scolding us thoroughly for our clumsiness on decompression, removed the last embarrassment of the sink episode by showing me a third *Remipede*, caught in Sagittarius. The caves were a zoo!

49 (*top*) *Remipedia*, the new class of crustacean from Bahamian caves
50 (*centre*) A Barbouria shrimp, a characteristic cave entrance dweller
51 (*above*) *Lucifuga spelaeotes*, the blind Bahamian cave-fish

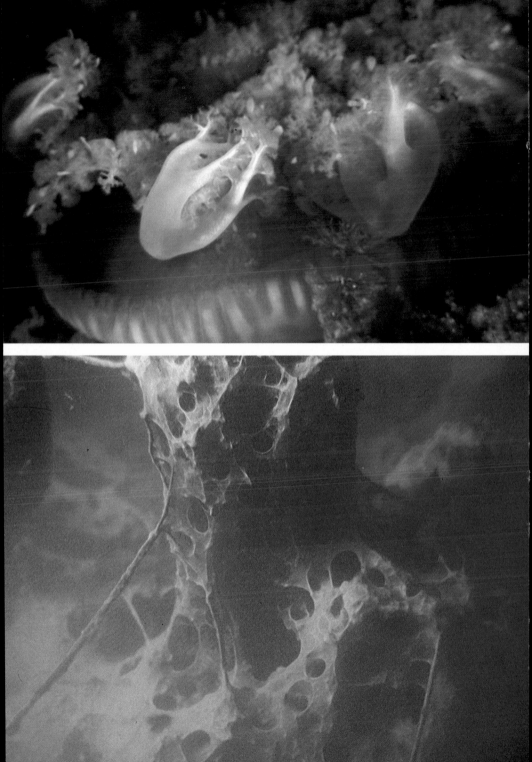

52 (*opposite left*) 'Inverted' Cassiopeia jellyfish swarmed in the shallow lakes

53 (*opposite below*) The lakes could have been a setting for a Hammer horror film

54 (*right*) Deep in Pisces, a serpulid worm filters the cave water in search of food

55 (*below*) A serpulid worm tube winds its way across the rocks of Pisces

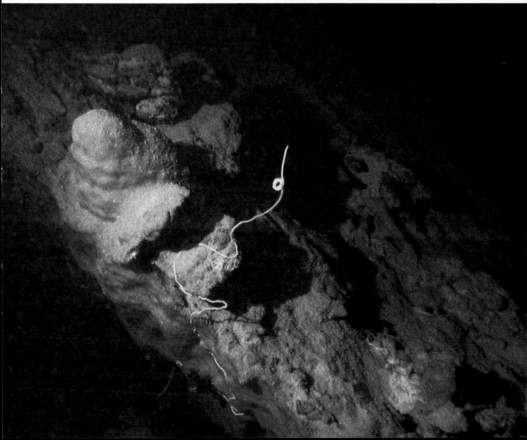

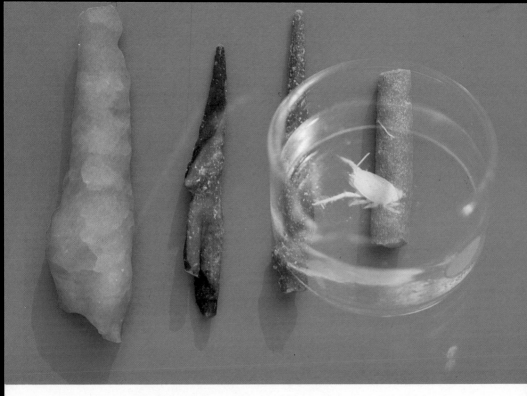

56 Clean and tannic-stained speleothems, with the mythical 'cave-crab' haunting the scene

57 (*below left*) A thermosbanacean, one of the tiny cave crustaceans, barely four millimetres long

58 (*below right*) A Cirolanid isopod from Asgard

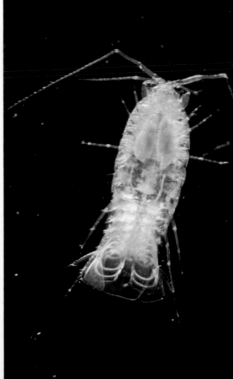

8

The Ice Queen's Palace

Three thousand watts of light illuminated Virgo. A distant glow heralded the sight, tantalising our sense of expectation as we swam along the arched passage at the foot of the entrance shaft. Three tiny *Remipedia* danced a many-legged jig in silhouette around a stalagmite as we turned the corner and gazed, spellbound, at the sight.

The underwater cave in the first tentative probings of exploration, by the light of tiny torches, had been a mysterious, half-seen country, inhabited by the insubstantial wraiths of our mental unease. The same cave in brighter hand-held light had become more homely, bounded by solid walls. The wraiths had taken substance, defined by cold logic instead of atavistic concern.

But fill the cave with the fixed light of three cold suns and it becomes a city of unparalleled splendour, castellated towers rising from a hillside of flowing rock to a high and vaulted roof. The sight is humbling and awe-inspiring. In the water, suspended above the stone city, we were stunned by the wealth, the complex hues and shapes of nature, the slow hidden artistry we were so profoundly privileged to see.

The lights had gone in smoothly, without any major hitches. Rob and Julian had descended the cave with a camera, watches synchronised with Peter's on the surface.

The seconds ticked by. At 1.33.50, Julian pointed the camera at Rob and switched it on. At 1.34.00 exactly, Peter flipped the generator switch on the surface. The caves filled with light for the first time in their existence, leaving both divers gasping at the sudden change.

It felt peculiar to be swimming in so much light. There was an illusion of flight, spoilt only by inevitable clouds of sediment that rose from the floor, or drifted down from niches in the walls and roof above, disturbed by rising air bubbles. The water was layered, divided into horizontal bands by thermoclines within the cave. Often the change was too insignificant to be felt by divers passing through each layer but the shimmering out of focus intermixture that resulted was a certain giveaway. It was enough of a hindrance to human vision, inducing instant myopia, but it played absolute havoc with Peter's filming and our photography.

Peter coped with his frustration well. All his sequences were planned out on the surface before a dive and put into action as quickly as possible underwater. There was only the chance for one or, at the most, two takes. After that, he had to fall back on random grab-shots, moving around the cavern, trying to stay one step ahead of both silt and shimmer.

The lights were set up in the 'Red Room', the sloping chamber on the right of the crossroads just inside the entrance. The formations in the room were coated with a fine, red dust, staining many of them a light rusty shade. Moving straight ahead at the crossroads, an ascending passage led into the 'White Room', where a pure white grotto crowned the slope. Why the two chambers should differ was a mystery.

With the lights blazing, the cave was far safer. If we swam with reasonable care, the water remained reasonably clear, and we learned to navigate around the familiar cave with ease. With four divers in the cave on filming trips, Peter and Georgie had a more than adequate safety cover if anything should go wrong.

By now we were beginning to realise something of the importance, in biological terms, of the Caverns. At least three different species of *Remipedia* had been discovered, and a surprising number of other crustaceans had been captured in collection bags as well. Sagittarius was proving the most exciting site, a cryptic cave environment that differed in many respects from the other caves.

Remipedia had been thoroughly filmed in close-up, in tanks and 'O' ring traps in the A-frame. Peter was now keen to film the creature *in situ* in the caves or, if this failed, at least to film the capture of a specimen. With the hazy intermixture, we had little time to hunt. We decided on a devious plan whereby, should no 'Little Crittur' be instantly available, Sarah and I would establish ourselves in a medium-sized cloud of sediment, point excitedly at the largest lump and capture it in a jar, while Peter filmed us. Cut to shot of a *Remipede* in a tank. Who says the camera never lies?

We did this a couple of times, chasing *Remipede*-sized lumps of rock realistically through the water, until guilt became too much for me. As Peter swam over to his equipment pile to replace an exhausted film light, I beckoned Sarah and Georgie down to deeper, clearer water. I had been getting the knack of spotting animals down to a fine art and felt that realism was, in local parlance, 'mo' bettah'.

By the time Peter returned, a swimming centipede was dancing in front of my outstretched finger, gently herded around in a pool of light. Peter's eyes shone. The camera whirred, the rock was released, and replaced by the *Remipede* in the jar, after a very authentic chase. Another sequence was in the can.

Sagittarius was the only major cave in Lake One. In 1983 Rob Parker had explored about 400 metres of passages, ending beneath a small opening in the woods behind the village, though he had not attempted to surface. The cave ran away from the major collapse zone surrounding the lakes and seemed to have avoided much of the cataclysmic destruction of the aston stage. If any of us had had to choose the most beautiful of the Zodiac Caverns, it would have been Sagittarius.

When we arrived in 1984, Rob was still the only person to have seen the cave in its entirety. I had been with Anitra Thorhaug to a small deep chamber about fifty metres in and could remember a pure white flowstone cascade down one wall, much thick silt in the entrance, but little else. In his usual taciturn way, Rob had mentioned that the rest of the cave was rather well-decorated, but his quiet comments had been lost in the vocal enthusiasm that Julian and I had had for Virgo at the time.

One by one, Rob took the others into Sagittarius: Sarah to collect specimens; Peter, Georgie and Julian to film. All came out rather bemused, with stories of the most exquisite chambers of all, of clear perfect visibility, of a flourishing fauna that followed curious patterns of distribution. I was too involved with Pisces and the problems of day to day logistics to manage an early dive there, and began to feel that I was missing something. One day when I had some free time I was able to follow the filming team in, collect water samples for Lucy and see the cave for myself.

Peter, Rob and Julian were surfacing as I arrived, having prospected a site for the 1,000 watt lights. Rob pointed out where the guideline began, and I swam down through the drifting mists of their exit into a half-remembered wide and silty tunnel. Sweeping fin marks cut into the sediments, a reminder of the crisis when Peter had discovered water inside his Arriflex housing and had exited the cave at high speed to save the expensive camera inside. The sharp gouges in the floor revealed a clear layering of sediments, the result of a gentle rain of debris unimaginably old. A tripod lay where he had abandoned it, under an obscuring film of silt. I shook it clear, sticking it vertically in the sediment where it would be easier to locate on the way out.

The Ice Queen's Palace

Shuffle-finning over the silt banks, I passed the jumpline into the deep chamber that marked my previous limit in the cave. Shortly after that I began to realise what I had been missing. Despite the blurred visibility caused by the previous visitors, the outlines of the cave could be clearly seen. I came to a junction in the line and turned left, following Rob's directions. On either side fragile columns rose between roof and floor, curiously different to those I had seen elsewhere. It took me a moment or two to understand why. The lower sections were white, virtually clean calcite, but the tops were a solid entwining mass of serpulid tubes, a ridiculously complex coat of fragile tubes that in places seemed to be two or three centimetres thick! How many generations of worms had been responsible for such a polychæte metropolis? So densely had they grown on some of the speleothems that they had caused them to collapse beneath their mounting weight, to lie in shards across the floor. This serpulid profusion seemed to happen only above a certain depth and was virtually absent in some chambers. Why should they choose one site and not another? Was it a reaction to some local enrichment of the cave waters, from overhead percolation or slight horizontal flow. Was it to do with oxygen levels in the water, or subtle variations in the temperature? We are still not sure.

Beyond two groups of slender formations, a perfect gour pool nestled in the floor. Here was nature at her most surrealistic, a fragile crystal pool, filled with supersaturated water in the distant dry past of the cave. Some of the saturated water had evaporated in the gentle air currents, tens of thousands of years ago, and sharp, pure crystals of calcite had grown in the base of the pool as the mineral came out of solution. Before moving on, I traced a finger across the smooth, sharp crystals that bristled in the hollow.

At set points, I stopped and filled small plastic bottles with uncontaminated cave water for Lucy, who was trying to establish salinity and temperature profiles of the cave. We were still searching a little unsuccessfully for a thick, established lens of freshwater. There was a thin one near the village, which had been badly contaminated by an ill-designed pumping scheme several years before. This should overlie Sagittarius, but so far it showed no presence in the cave. Compared to others, Sagittarius was deep. Throughout its length, it ran in and out of the ancient twenty to twenty-five metre level of the original cave formation of the Zodiac System. Though there was some breakdown on the floor, the passages largely retained their old phreatic shape, little altered over several hundred centuries. Swimming in suspended flight across a succession of halls, each more sumptuously decorated than the last, I finally came to the crystal cavern chosen for the film lights. Beyond this lay the third entrance, the small hole in the woods.

Ducking over a collapsed block on which a series of calcite curtains lay in chipped and angled folds, unnaturally askew to their original line of growth, I came to the first scatterings of silt – loose organic debris that lay in patches between the formations on the floor. Out of curiosity, I left the line and rose a few metres up the slope at the side. Barbouria shrimps scampered in the silt. The lower entrance water, stained a tannic brown, was full of tiny crustaceans: thermosbanaceans and ostracods, the detritivores of the cave, making the most of this high-energy environment. Peculiar chemical layering in the water lent a fey touch to the scene, grey spiral whorls in horizontal bands. One, stranger than the rest, resembled a long triangular prism, an inexplicable phenomenon. They looked like similar forms seen on Andros, in an unusually organic inland hole. Dim daylight filtered down through the brown water and I crept cautiously up to a depth of nine metres below the entrance. As I took a water sample, an acid, sulphurous taste stole round the mouthpiece of my regulator. I backed out carefully, leaving the entrance for another day.

In the clear corroded chambers at the far end of the line, I took a final sample, trapped two ostracods, microscopic pea-shaped creatures, and retraced my path, returning to the main entrance of the cave to decompress in the warm daylight below the lake.

A few days later the cable lights came out of Virgo and went into Sagittarius. Because the chosen chamber was so far from the main entrance the cable had to go through the tiny entrance in the woods. This was less straightforward than it seemed. Rob Parker thought it impossible to get close enough to the surface to pass the cable out, and the entrance looked too constricted to pass the cable, with the bulky light units attached, in from the outside. They would have to be carried all the way from the lake entrance. Rob and Julian raked the bush around the A-frame for pieces of timber long enough to lash together and poke up the slope with the cable securely lashed on. They finally disappeared into the cave with a Heath Robinson assortment of bits, Rob carrying an enormous tacklebag containing the three lamps, with a buoyancy jacket strapped to it to give it extra lift. Julian followed close behind with the coils of cable and the disassembled poles.

Peter and Leo waited outside the woodland entrance. At last, bubbles from the exhaust of the divers below broke the water's surface. Peter bent down to peer into the hole. Suddenly he sprang back as the pole rose, like Excalibur, from the depths, trailing the wire behind. Filming with the big lamps was now possible in Sagittarius.

Dennis Williams made several visits to our exploration sites out of curiosity. He had several years more scientific experience than us and this, together with an inherent laziness, had led him to develop various collection systems that allowed him to catch or record more on one dive than we could on several. He guarded his hoard of gadgetry jealously, tantalising us with a 'look but don't play' approach. He was more than happy to work it himself when there, and went in with Sarah and Howard Cosgrove, another local cave-diver, to make a collection run in Sagittarius.

Dennis's machine was super-efficient: the creatures stood no chance! They were sucked from the water down a tube, passed through a non-return valve, and deposited in a jar. Back at the A-frame, he emptied his haul in a bowl.

'We have', he announced efficiently, 'at least three species of *Remipedia* here. This one [poking a long and spindly variety] looks like *Speleonectes lucayensis*, the one from Lucayan Caverns. Probably the same. These two are different [prodding two squirming creatures into separate jars]. They look a bit like some of the ones we found last year in the Turks and Caicos Islands, but these aren't quite so big.'

He put them under the microscope and started counting legs. This seemed to be the best field method for distinguishing one species from the next. One of the unidentified types had about fifteen pairs of legs, the other somewhere in the twenties. Dennis thought that the stubbier variety might be a form of *Speleonectes robustus*, which grew much larger in the Turks and Caicos Islands, 'big enough to fry', as he put it. The other, a more graceful creature, resembled one they had nicknamed 'Beauty'. Only detailed examination in more sophisticated laboratory conditions could identify them with any certainty.

Scattered in the haul were thermosbanaceans and ostracods, the small crustacean detritivores that lived lower down the food chain, eating organic debris, smaller plankton or bacteria in the water. The ostracods, which in close-up looked like a jolly cartoon creature from a children's book – a bean with a feather in its cap – swam everywhere in the far cave, propelling themselves along in spurts with their tiny, feather-like appendages.

In the open sea, ostracods are extremely common, tiny nectonic creatures that exist at all depths from the surface to over 2,000 metres. Most are bottom-dwellers although, as in the caves, there are some free-swimming forms. Their fossil record stretches back over 500 million years and they are the most extensive of any crustacean group. Over 2,000 species have been identified in both saltwater and freshwater. Their ability to adapt to such a wide range of conditions makes them ideal candidates for cave life.

Thermosbanaceans are a little more enigmatic. Only half a dozen species are known, all of them subterranean in one form or another. *Thermosbaena mirabilis* lives in hot Tunisian springs at 48 degrees centigrade, while the *monodella* species inhabits fresh and brackish water in Mediterranean caves. A single species of *monodella* comes from freshwater caves in Texas, but the Bahamian variety so far lacks formal identification.

As far as anyone knows, thermosbanaceans are detritivores, their mouth-parts being adapted to bite into large particles or to scrape up many smaller bits. Female thermosbanaceans carry four to ten eggs at a time in a 'brood-pouch', an enlargement of their carapace. Newly-hatched young are virtually identical to their parents, save for the last pair of legs, which appears after subsequent moults.

This ability to protect their young while at a critical stage of development could be an important one. In the competitive, low-energy environment of an underwater cave, free-floating eggs would be a rich meal, and newly-hatched larvae would find the hunt for nourishment exceedingly difficult. By the time the tiny crustaceans leave their brood-pouches, whether amphipod, isopod or thermosbanacean, they have at least a certain degree of mobility that gives them a start in an environment in which, at the best of times, it is an unrelenting struggle to survive.

Even the serpulid fan-worms can choose to fertilise their eggs in the parent tube. Under parental protection until the free-swimming larval stage, they are better able to survive in the dark environment than the planktonic larvae of sponges, corals or decapod crustaceans – the lobsters, shrimps and crabs.

No less significant a step on the way to cave-adaptation is the ability to find a mate at all, and breed successfully in such hostile conditions of total darkness. Some complicated chemical and tactile sensory process could be at work here, identifying genders and avoiding predators.

News of a final inhabitant of the caves we (luckily or unluckily) failed to encounter was revealed one day to Jill Yager as she waited for us by the lake: if you went to the lake at night, alone (said one of the young village girls in all seriousness), you might be met by one of the mermaids that live in the beautiful castles beneath the lake. The mermaid would ask if you ate fish and if you were foolish enough to say yes she would drag you by your hair below the water, to drown. If you said no she would take you instead to her beautiful underwater home, and there cut off a lock of her hair and give it to you to keep. Hide this close and tell no living soul, and good fortune, riches and a happy marriage would follow. Breathe a word of what you had seen, or show the lock of hair to another, and you were for ever cursed.

The animals were definite about their preferred choice of habitat. There were two distinct layers of water in Sagittarius, warmer above colder, as in Aquarius and the other Caverns. Both layers were inhabited, but a slight temperature difference (around 1 degree centigrade) and a slight difference in clarity suggested that the upper layer carried whatever water flow there was. Immeasurable it might be to us, it was there nevertheless. There was little discernible difference in salinity between the layers, but *Remipedia* seemed to prefer the lower of the two, venturing into the warmer zone only occasionally, possibly to hunt. The thermosbanaceans and ostracods seemed less particular, moving at will between the two, though also appearing to favour the deeper cave. Whether they spent their entire existence in open passage was another matter. Some species of each type inhabit sediments in the outside world, and it was possible that the amphipods as well might be more at home in the silt on the floor. In dry caves many of the microfaunal inhabitants seek shelter and food in the tiny cracks and crevices that lead from an open passage.

There are good reasons for this. These are the complex three-dimensional micro-conduits by which much of the food material enters the cave in the first place, washed down by the pressures of percolating rainwater. For detritivores, whose diet is composed of such organic material, plant or animal, these channels are obvious feeding grounds. They also provide a certain protection from predators. We noticed on several occasions that cave creatures pursued by collecting jars made for the safety of a confined crevice. In the case of *Lucifuga*, this was with apparently practised aim, suggesting that the blind fish might have some established territorial awareness.

There appeared to be an established order of predation, with *Lucifuga* and *Remipedia* near the top of the chain. To what extent the rest of the inhabitants preyed on each other was impossible to say, though we suspected that the thermosbanaceans and ostracods might be rather low down on the pecking order of the cave hunters.

We did little collection in the cave sediments, keeping our attention on the deep cave, free-swimming population. By doing this, we undoubtedly missed much.

One day Lucy and I returned, hot and well-bitten, from an afternoon of surface survey to find Dennis and Sarah sieving through the afternoon's haul, in close session with Jill Yager, recently returned from a Californian study session. They appeared engrossed in their work, as did everyone else in the A-frame. It was a busy scene, with everybody beavering away at their own devices.

I collapsed on a chair in chauvinistic sloth while Lucy made the coffee. In front of me on the table was a large glass jar. I looked idly at the creature inside, and then picked it up and looked more closely. Eagerly, I collared Rob and asked what it was.

'Oh, that,' he said casually, 'we found it in the sediment after today's filming dive.'

I became excited. It looked like a blind, white, cave-adapted hermit crab. Jill promptly said she had never seen anything like it in a cave before. Dennis agreed that its atrophied eyes, the feathery hairs on its legs, and its pigmentless body and shell looked thoroughly cave-adapted, like a creature that existed by touch alone in a dark and hostile world. Perhaps we had been wrong to ignore the sediments!

Peter (who had, in fact, dug the crab out of the sand in the beach in front of the house) appeared with his (empty) Arriflex, tripod, lights, tanks and stands, and proceeded to 'film' the animal. I was utterly taken in and spent the next hour photographing it from every angle, becoming increasingly excited. Every now and again, someone would have to leave the room, unable to keep a straight face any longer.

It was two days before Sarah, unwilling to put up further with my rummagings around silt banks and my eager exhortations to search for more on every dive, broke the news gently. Feeling thoroughly ashamed of my own eagerness for the hunt, I kept very quiet about cave life for several days after that. Dennis later took great glee in pointing out that no one ever said they found it in the cave, or did anything but agree with me on the characteristics of the beastie. I had fooled myself beautifully!

Peter's filming in Sagittarius went well. The chamber, when lit by the three lamps, was a fairyland of crystal, an Ice Queen's Palace, giving us an unparalleled opportunity to examine the structure of the cave closely. Because the lights were set at a level of twenty-two metres, under a twenty-metre ceiling, they just escaped the effect of the main mixing zone a few metres higher. There was far less of a shimmer of intermixture to cope with.

The focal point of the lights was a cascading bank of formations in one corner of the room. As we swam towards the cavern along the main cave, in the comparative darkness of our smaller hand-lights, a distant glow silhouetted the angles of the passage ahead. The way into the chamber was through a smaller opening near the roof at one side and the sudden change was spellbinding.

The Ice Queen's Palace

The hall was about fifteen metres in diameter and could accommodate four or five divers without each getting too much in another's way. The formations tumbled down across the chaos of etched and fallen boulders, a lush covering of snow-white icing on the soft, corroded rock. All the classic speleothem forms were there, unchanged for the fifty thousand years since their creation, clean and pure, without trace of stain or sediment. Stalagmite pillars over a metre high and thick as an arm, rose from the flowstone cascade in the foreground. Above each was a counterpart, either a slender stalactite, or a rippled curtain of translucent calcite, banded by subtle changes in chemistry or growth, a flowing, folded sheet of tapering crystal only millimetres thick. In the centre, thick columns stretched from roof to floor where stalactites had descended to meet the tips of their partners long before. Thin soda-straws, unimaginably delicate, grew in clusters on the roof between the pillars. Each hollow centre of the fragile straws was filled with saltwater, no longer an inner pathway for the slow, measured drips of percolation water to trickle down. At the back of the cascade, supported only by their own brittle crystalline structure, stalagmite pillars rose almost to the roof, nearly three metres high, with bare centimetres of space between their tips and the rock above.

The sight would have been magical in a dry cave. Here, in the clear underwater chamber, where we could glide around and examine it from every angle, it was above description. Without a doubt, all of us could have hung there for hours, drowning in the luxury of the sight and seeking small nuances of beauty in each shining corner of the cavern.

9

Dancers in the Twilight Zone

Devon looked at the three mongrels squabbling in the undergrowth, the two dogs vying for the bitch in heat.

'Dem dogs,' he said, with all the seriousness of a seven-year-old making man-talk, 'Dey always make fuss, stickin' togedder like dat.'

Our dives in Sagittarius attracted a growing audience of local kids now school was out for the summer. To reach the cave, we would kit up on the concrete pier, stagger through the village square and along a rough path through the undergrowth behind the school to a small rocky outcrop on the edge of the lake. By that time, it was good to get in the water and make the final adjustments to equipment in the lake itself.

Devon was a persistent helper, entranced by everything we did. With his aunt Natasha, fully a year older than himself, he would pick up any loose item and trot along-side, engaging us in earnest conversation. Within a few days he became adept at noticing minor oversights in our equipment checks, and would embarrass individual members of the team by stridently pointing out checks they had forgotten. His favourite was Rob Parker, who always seemed more willing than the rest of us to put up with his incessant chatter. Devon quickly became the unofficial mascot of the expedition.

Extracting my camera and flash from his little hands, and replacing them with a less fragile pair of fins, we tottered through the undergrowth to the others. Peter and Georgie, Rob and Sarah, had already left, and Mary Brooks, joining us for the day, was struggling into her fins in the water. Mary, for several years a cave-diving instructor in Freeport before moving to Deep Water Cay, was one of America's most experienced female cave-divers. This was her first dive in the Zodiac Caverns and she was looking forward to it enthusiastically. Short and slight, she looked dwarfed by the two back-mounted 80s she wore in U.S. style.

Peter was still trying to film *Remipedia in situ* in the cave and, if he could sneak up on them carefully enough, the shy serpulid worms. Eventually he set up his camera on one particular tube and left it standing in the cave overnight, before creeping back the next day, lighting it from a distance and gently switching the camera on. That finally did the trick.

Mary and I set out on a photographic dive, with the added intention of collecting a series of water samples in the far entrance, as near to the surface as possible. I felt guilty as we swam into the cave. The marks of heavy passage were everywhere, from the gouged fin-marks of Peter's camera flood in the sediments, to broken speleothems along the route. No matter how carefully we moved, each of us had collided at some time with one or more of the formations. Whenever a sickening tell-tale crunch and echoing tinkle reverberated through the water, we were aware that another act of irreparable destruction had taken place in a second of human clumsiness. It was like moving blindfolded through a room of crystal chandeliers, all at different heights, and all suspended by single threads. On more than one occasion, thin pillars would collapse without even being touched, tumbling in awful slow-motion through the water, shattering on impact into a dozen pieces. So delicately were they constructed that even the wake of our passage was too much for the crystal structure to cope with. In some cases, the added weight of the serpulid tubes exacerbated the situation. I caught one as it started to fall, and floated without moving, ten thousand years of crystal growth balanced in one hand in a futile gesture. There was nothing I could do but open my fingers and let the inevitable proceed. We brought out fragments of the wreckage to keep for sophisticated age-dating on our return to Britain. At least the unhappy destruction might serve some cause.

Mary's emotions on seeing the powerful lighting in the cave were profound. She floated in the chamber, shaking her head and holding out her hands helplessly. The room was one of the finest underwater chambers in the system and for Mary, used as she was to blue hole diving, the sight was an exquisite experience.

We swam in single file down the cave and into passages rarely visited by the diving team. It was obvious we were having an effect on the biota as well. The passages here were rich with life, whereas our regular routes had become barren by comparison. Regular human presence was obviously driving the tiny fauna into hiding and only in the quieter sections were they active in their usual profusion. At the base of the woodland entrance I signalled Mary to wait by the line while I ascended the slope of rotting debris to sample water for Lucy in the odd, chemical zone.

That too had been affected. The curious banding was now virtually absent, disturbed by the toing and froing of cables. As I rose up, determined to surface if possible, the sulphurous taste crept into my mouth again as the waters turned a rich, deep brown. Large chunks of leaf matter and rotten branches rained down as I ascended, a disorientating shower in the dark, organic water.

I pushed aside a crumbling branch and tried in vain to force a way around a large rock that blocked the entrance. Without stripping the equipment from my waist, it was impossible. My outstretched fingers could touch the surface from below, just close enough for Peter, waiting above, to take the line from me and tie it off outside. I sank

59 Sarah Cunliffe negotiates her way gingerly through a speleothem forest

60 (*left*) Rob Parker, in the film-lights of Sagittarius

61 (*below*) Peter Scoones with his camera in Sagittarius

62 (*opposite right*) A gour pool in Sagittarius, filled with water when the cave was dry

63 (*opposite below*) A snow-white cascade of crystal – the filming chamber in Sagittarius

64 Sarah Cunliffe peers between crystal pillars in Sagittarius

65 Sarah Cunliffe floats in front of the crystal grotto in Sagittarius

back down the slope in a cloud of debris, leaving the gleam of daylight behind, and returned to join Mary as she waited patiently by the line.

We joined Rob and Sarah in decompression in the early sunset. Above our heads, a school of mosquito fish danced in the flickering reflections, scattering as a shoal of half-beaks, with their thin, streamlined snouts, swam by. The surface, broken by our bubbles, flashed a host of tiny rainbows back. Strange, unidentified, bewhiskered fish peered from tight crevices among the rocks of the entrance, and orange nematode worms writhed in knotted, communal orgies in the algal fronds.

Only the rhythmic sound of our breathing broke the evening stillness until, one by one, we rose, left the cave behind, and swam towards the waiting children on the shore.

We could hardly have chosen a less auspicious day for Leo's skydive into Manta Hole than Friday the thirteenth.

Though a veteran of several hundred skydives, many in difficult, not to say original circumstances, Leo had never parachuted into water. Before leaving Britain, however, he sought advice from military friends who had done so. They looked at him somewhat askance. It was, they said, one of the most dangerous jumps to make. There were two things that could go wrong. On touchdown, you had to release the canopy. Things went wrong if you released it too soon, or too late; the exact moment to 'cut-away' was crucial. Normally releasing the parachute (cutting-away) is the last thing a parachutist does, and then only in an emergency. In water jumping it is essential, ideally done the moment before impact, just as your feet are about to touch the water. Do it too late, or not at all, and the weight of the wet canopy might drag the parachutist down under the surface to drown. Do it too soon – and this seemed to be the real temptation – and the sudden extra speed of the unsupported fall could easily result in a broken leg, or worse.

Manta Hole in Big Creek was the biggest, deepest blue hole we could find. It gave Leo an area approximately thirty metres by twenty metres to aim for, quite a large target for a skydiver of his experience using a precisely-steerable 'square-rig', a popular type of parachute which allows the user a high degree of directional control. If conditions were right, he *ought* to be able to land in the boat, though that was the last thing we wanted. I played down my encounter with the giant moray eel in this hole the previous year.

All the same, Leo could not stop worrying about the possibility that he might miss – less on account of professional pride than because the surrounding terrain was, as he put it, 'vicious limestone with holes in it, and sharp edges!' Were he to catch his foot in a hole, he risked at the very least a broken ankle; if he should be dragged across it, his injuries would be serious. It was, he said, the worst possible place he could imagine to visit by parachute. Also, as he pointed out, statistics showed that a great number of people had come to grief on water jumps, many of them more experienced than he. Our cave-diving might be an extreme application of underwater exploration, but did we realise that skydiving into a blue hole was just as extreme an aspect of his chosen sport?

The episode had to be planned with meticulous care. The camera Leo chose to use was the most robust he had, a Photosonic, designed to withstand conditions that would destroy a normal camera. This went inside a waterproof housing which had survived a descent of the Dudh Kosi, the highest and one of the fiercest rivers in the world, flowing from the snows of the Western Cwm of Everest. After that, it ought to survive the shock of a blue hole landing.

It was essential for Leo to have safety cover both in and out of the water. We decided that Sarah, Rob and Julian would be in the Zodiac inflatable, positioned on the downwind side of the hole, serving a dual role as wind-sock. Rob and Julian would be fully kitted up, as though about to dive in the cave, and would leap into the water as soon as Leo touched down, to render any assistance that might be necessary. I would be already underwater, about ten metres in front of the boat with another camera, both to film the splashdown from below, and to provide additional emergency cover. The others (except for Peter) would be onshore, filming the landing from the side. Peter's place was in the plane with Leo; we could not waste the opportunity of filming the island from above, giving a visual perspective to the area we were exploring.

This seemed quite simple at the early planning stage. In the event it required much fine timing and careful organisation to ensure it came off perfectly. Leo and Peter were duly despatched to Freeport to meet Dennis and the plane, and would duly reappear the following day, Friday the thirteenth, 1,000 metres up in the skies above Big Creek.

A hiccup in the procedure occurred when we discovered that Dennis would be unable to return Peter to East End the following day, after the plane had returned to Freeport. I scouted round Sweeting's Cay to find someone who would be in town the next day. Big Ben Russell, our usual source of lifts, had taken his truckful of conch into town that morning but his neighbour was only too happy to oblige. I met him and asked how Peter would be able to recognise him. He pointed to his gaudy hat with a rude slogan embroidered across the peak.

'I'll be wearin' dis hat, mahn,' he beamed, 'outside de supermarket.'

This was a shade embarrassing. The only telephone in the area was in the minister's house in MacLean's Town. I took the whaler over early on Friday morning, hoping that the telephone would be working and that he would be out. No such luck. Reverend Pinder sat dozing in his favourite armchair, straight across from the telephone. To make matters worse, I had a bad line and needed to shout.

'How do I recognise this guy?' asked Peter.

'He'll be wearing a red-and-white hat,' I replied.

'That cuts it down a bit.'

'It says, "I'm so horny I get excited by the crack of dawn." '

'What? Can't hear you.'

'I'M SO HORNY I GET EXCITED BY THE CRACK OF DAWN.'

Reverend Pinder blinked and woke up. He looked at me reproachfully. I smiled weakly back.

'O.K., no problem,' said Peter.

Everyone was extremely efficient on the appointed morning, hiding their apprehension. We anchored the boats in Big Creek at 10.30 a.m., in good time to ensure that everything would be ready. Georgie, Mandy and Lucy were onshore, moving from place to place in search of the best camera angle. I hauled my gear to the water's edge and took the whaler off to hide it beneath an overhanging mangrove bush at the far end of the bay. By midday we were all waiting, ready to go. Storm clouds flashed sheet lightning between us and Freeport but the conditions in Big Creek could hardly have been better. A gentle breeze blew from the south, and the sky above was clear.

Julian looked out across the hole and said, in a slightly concerned tone, 'I think I just saw a fin in the water.'

Everybody looked. Nothing. People looked away again. A moment later, a sharp black fin and a sleek expanse of back rose out of the water and then sank.

'He's right,' I said from the water, suddenly feeling vulnerable, 'I saw it too.'

Rob, Julian and Sarah stared at me from the boat.

'I don't think it was very big,' said Julian, uncertainly.

I wasn't so sure. It had seemed rather sizeable to me. Sharks don't *have* to be very big to hurt and I made the mistake of pointing this out. They looked at me seriously.

'You'd better go and have a look then, in case it's too dangerous for Leo to jump.'

I gazed uneasily at Julian and suggested that I wasn't sure it was any part of the responsibility of leadership to offer myself as bait. Why didn't he go? He pointed out that I was in the water already. I felt I could soon solve that if they made some more room in the boat. They looked at me sternly. Shamefaced, and somewhat scared, I made a very cautious circuit of the hole, with a lurking sensation of being watched. A vicious-looking barracuda slunk in the shallows at the far side of the cave but there was no sign of the shark. Either it was inside the cave or it had gone.

Leo, in the meantime, was up in the air. As they had climbed into the small plane, Dennis had casually offered the information that he had never watched a parachutist leap out of his plane before. (He had actually flown parachutists before, one of whom had let off a smoke trailer in the cockpit and Dennis, eyes streaming and nose centimetres from the instruments, trying to see what was happening to the plane, had suddenly realised that he was alone in the cabin. It was, he said, a very peculiar feeling.)

This announcement did little to reassure Leo. As they flew out over the island, dodging the thunderstorms and descending at one point to below 600 metres to avoid low clouds, he grew apprehensive that he might not be able to jump from his desired height. Eventually they flew into clearer sky and saw the boat far below. Dropping a streamer to check the speed and direction of the wind, they circled the bay.

Down in Big Creek, the sight of the plane galvanised us into action. Rob and Julian hastily strapped on their remaining gear while I, still nervous, slipped beneath the water and lay on the bottom of the hole, ten metres in front of the boat. In my own personal quandary, I didn't want to miss Leo's touchdown and had my eyes glued on the Zodiac inflatable. But I kept wanting to look over my shoulder, certain that there was something there.

Oblivious to sharks, Leo squeezed into the doorway of the Cessna, ready to jump, very aware that we had only one good chance to get everything right. Trying to organise the jump again would be very difficult. As far as he was concerned, we were a crew of people who would rather be down caves than waiting for unorthodox cameramen to land on top of them.

He climbed out on to the strut, gave a big grin to

Dennis, waved at Peter, fell out of the plane, and disappeared from their sight.

Not having an altimeter, he opened his canopy a little earlier than he intended. From on high, the small boat looked rather out of place in the surrounding sandy flats but, as he came lower, the scene slid into perspective and it all looked right.

Soaring in over the top of the Zodiac, Leo yelled with delight, and wondered why no one seemed to be watching.

'Of course,' he said later, 'they took not the slightest bit of notice, which is normally the case with eccentric cameramen anyway. Besides, they were being much more professional than I was, simply ignoring the camera so that it wouldn't ruin the shot.'

Zipping over the top of Julian's head, Leo was amazed to find that as he hit the water he bounced straight out again, the wind catching the parachute as his weight came off it momentarily. He immediately cut-away and splashed down. Rob and Julian followed him in and a moment later we all surfaced by the side of the boat together, a little stunned by the sudden climax to the episode.

From underwater the landing had looked superb. One moment, the surface above was merely rippled reflections of blue; the next, an enormous yellow and brown canopy filled the sky. It seemed to hang there for an age, slowly spreading until it encompassed my entire field of vision.

Then, suddenly, there had been a flurry in the water between me and the boat, and a further flurry as Rob and Julian tumbled in to help. Leo had been so precise in his landing that, as I surfaced with my camera still running, Sarah was struggling out from underneath the collapsed folds of canopy that had landed just behind him, across the bows of the boat. It had almost escaped getting wet!

Big Creek had captured our attention the year before. The blue holes which followed the line of a massive fracture along the side of the island in a long chain were the deepest we had yet discovered at East End. Julian and I had reached a depth of over fifty metres in Helm's Deep, and Rob had spiralled down below the huge twilight hall of Lothlorien to a choke thirty-two metres down. Out of thirty entrances we had explored only seven and wanted to see more. It would have been straining resources to mount a major push on the day of Leo's skydive so we used the opportunity to clear up loose ends in known caves.

Lothlorien is without doubt one of the most atmospheric of ocean blue holes. Light shines down its five entrances into the massive chamber we had investigated the year before. That afternoon we all went in: Rob and Julian to attempt the deep choke, the rest of us to photograph the hole.

The two explorers put great effort into their attempt to follow the current in the cave. At the deepest point their passage was obstructed by a fall of boulders, through which a descending continuation could be seen, a larger passage than the one leading down to it. They dug at the choke until their air ran low, taking turns to pull the rocks to one side. A moment of drama arose as Julian tried to worm his way past the loose blocks and became wedged. Rob was able to move in behind him and pull him free but the boulders shifted again to block the way on. Short of air, they abandoned the effort and retreated to the sunshine above.

Leo and Mandy, on their first cave-dive, came down with me. It was a safe enough site – daylight could be seen from any point in the chamber and it was easy to keep clear of the sand on the floor.

There was an added magic to the cave that day. The chamber was a mass of silversides, a flowing shoal of myriad tiny fish that thought and moved as one. We had a front seat for one of the most amazing shows of the sea as the massive shoal danced for us in the cavern waters. Ripples ran along its length as the fish pirouetted in unison. We joined the game, disappearing into the shoal, surrounded by a cloud of silver light. No matter how hard we tried, they were beyond our power to touch. We might as well have tried to clasp a ghost.

At length our air ran low and we had to leave the shining stream behind, cascading in a phantom, ceaseless ballet in the twilight cave.

10

The Lens Caverns

One evening near sunset, Lucy and I took the whaler and made our way up Big Water Creek, along the northern shore of Sweeting's Cay. The fringing pinewoods glowed with a low warm light that threw the shadow of the boat ahead of us across the transparent evening water. Dark round mounds of brain coral flashed by underneath us as the boat skimmed over a lake of light, a golden ocean, cast in the reflection of the sun.

Arcing widely around a sandbank, we passed the entrance to Zodiac Creek and followed a winding channel upstream through shallow banks of eelgrass. We headed towards a break in the trees on the Sweeting's Cay shore, a kilometre or so east of the Zodiac caves. On our aerial run over the island, several small lakes had been spotted in the pine forest and the darker hues in some of the lakes had suggested cave entrances. The pines themselves were an indicator of freshwater; where these grew, there had to be a lens. Was any lens on Sweeting's Cay deep enough to reach down into the caves? Or was the islet now so small that the lens scarcely existed, deep enough only to provide freshwater for shallow-rooted forest growth?

The colour of the water ahead changed from the azure blue of the deeper channel to the yellow-green of shallows over sand and grass. We waded barefoot across the last few dozen metres, pulling the boat behind us, keeping an eye on the creek bed for the dark outlines of sharp-spined sea-urchins. Looping the bow-line over a stout mangrove root, we stepped on to the rocky shore and looked into the thick undergrowth that floored the forest in front.

Breaks in the bedrock were easy to see. Where lakes occurred, the vegetation changed. Broad-leaved trees and shrubs replaced the tall Bahamian pine and clustered around the unusual presence of surface groundwater. We thrashed our way through the scrubby undergrowth towards the closest copse of thorn and mangrove, a few metres inshore. Pulling apart a tangle of vines, Lucy looked into a deep crevice under the near wall of the pond. A cave no doubt, but getting into it would be difficult for the whole cleft was protected by a natural and very effective barrier of rubbery and tangled mangrove roots.

Further inland, two other lakes proved more accessible. Lucy and I waded ankle deep through soft brown mud and peered down a sizeable opening at the edge of the pond. This could scarcely be called a *blue* hole; the peaty brown water of the lakes made a mockery of the term. Peter, in a moment of cynical mosquito-bitten frustration, had rechristened the land-locked entrances of Lake One the 'inland hell-holes', and the name fell immediately into expedition patois. It differentiated quite distinctly the cool, blue marine caves from the atmospheric but insect-ridden inland pits.

The brown water was a harbour of decay in which years of organic debris had stained the lakes a deep tannic shade. It provided the slithery mousse of organic material which carpeted these inland pools and swept in mobile banks into the maw of the caves. This 'mung' was two-thirds water, one-third fine rotting debris, but although it rose in undulating waves at the slightest provocation, it settled again almost immediately.

The presence of bromeliads, air-plants that nestled in the crooks of mangrove branches and high flowering shrubs and thorns, suggested that the water was fresh.

Lucy took from her camera-pack a small digital meter which gave an instant read-out of the salinity and temperature of the water. She put the probe in the lake and took a reading.

'Fresh,' she said, with satisfaction.

On the following day we hacked a decent path through the undergrowth from the anchorage to the third of the lakes. The thorny vines had torn at our legs so our second trip to the lake, with the diving gear, was made in wetsuits, despite the heat. While Lucy took a set of salinity readings across the pond, Rob Parker kitted up in the mangrove shallows by the shore. With the possibility of a lens cave beneath us, Rob clipped a set of sampling bottles to his belt. He would be entering the cave first, without a line, moving as carefully as he could down the entrance slope, taking water samples every few metres. I would follow immediately behind him with the guideline, not letting him out of my sight. This careful technique was essential for the purity of the samples we needed to obtain: the more movement in the water, the more the layers would intermix and give false readings. If there was a lens here, we wanted to know just how thick it was.

The water inside the cave was the colour of strong tea. It soaked up light like water in a sponge. Rob's lights, only a metre or two in front of me, were a faint glow. The rock and the few small stalactites on the roof were the same dull colour. It was hard, even as our eyes adjusted to the darkness, to gain any real impression of the size of our surroundings. As I floated above Rob, keeping as far from the mung on the floor as possible, a moray eel snaked between the boulders below, a strange sight this far ashore.

Suddenly, as the formations began to cluster more thickly, there was a shimmer in the water and everything became clear. It was as though someone had drawn a mask from our eyes and turned the lights on. We moved into crystal water, cool and blue.

As Rob screwed the lid down on his last bottle, he

waved me in front. I moved past, following the slope deeper into the cave. I had been half-aware of a few small white creatures in the tannic layer above the shimmer but here, in the clear underlying layer, they were everywhere. The sheer profusion of life made even Sagittarius seem like a desert. We swam deeper but the walls closed in. Twenty metres down, Rob and I found ourselves in a small solutional chamber, surrounded by fretted limestone walls and jagged boulders. Though we searched the base of the chamber, there seemed to be no way through. If there was a continuation, it lay somewhere in the dark, stained layer above us. Rob pointed to his sample bottles, then back up the line. I waved an acknowledgment and he headed back towards the entrance, leaving me alone in the cave.

I could not believe that this was all there was to the place. For one thing, a cave as small as this would have been infilled by sediment long ago; the entrance would certainly not be so large and open. The speleothems that grew in such profusion on the fallen boulders of the entrance slope showed that the collapse must at least pre-date the last rise in sea-level, over 15,000 years ago. It was not as if the cave was young, the breakdown recent. For another thing, the sheer numbers of cave creatures suggested a deeper, more complex system. This numerous diversity would be unlikely to develop so close to the entrance of such a small cave. There was more life here than we had seen anywhere. Could we find a way large enough to get through?

For a quarter of an hour I explored every possible lead on the left-hand side of the chamber. In many places, the roof simply dropped to meet the mung. In others, grilles of stalagmite barred the way. Pushing myself through the sediment into the most hopeful opening, I waited for a cloud of organic flakes to settle. As the water cleared, I could see that the passage continued ahead into brown obscurity, too low to follow. I shuffled back with difficulty into the main passage as Rob's lights reappeared through the gloom. We moved across to the other side of the slope and continued the search. The right-hand wall looked little different at the top, a jumble of blocks, banked with brown mung.

At last, just above the shimmering halocline, I edged into a low restriction, reaching a place where I could look down into a slightly larger passage. There, the sediments seemed thinner. I paused for a moment to unhook a snarl of line from my tank valve and looked behind for Rob. He had given up the search and gone.

One last attempt. I squeezed into a delicate region of frail pillars between the floor and roof of a narrow horizontal gap. Eventually the crystal forms barred my way. Beyond, the cave could be seen to level off and increase in size. This *was* the way. It came to a point of decision. A sharp blow opened a route through the calcite bars that kept me from the cave, a sacrifice to the gods of exploration. Light danced along the walls as my torches reflected from the upper surface of the halocline. The passage opened up and I followed its left-hand wall above a deep canyon. In the upper cave, to my right, an absurd forest of columns clustered so closely together that there appeared to be more calcite than water in the chamber. They lay, unfortunately, in the tannic layer and their sheen was dulled to a light ochre by the brown waters.

The passage undulated in and out of the halocline, or so it appeared. The abrupt change from dark to clear water seemed too sudden for a simple change in temperature, and the huge increase in life below the shimmer suggested a major difference in the layers. Throughout the cave, the level of the change was the same, thirteen metres down.

As my line ran low on the reel, I came to an upward slope. It rose steeply into a low, flat chamber, barely a metre high. The depth gauge read only three metres. All that seemed to be holding the roof up was a huge central column, thicker than the cave was high. Light brown silt, very fine, filled small hollows and crevices in the floor. My bubbles disturbed plant material in roof cracks. The cave was very close to the surface, an aston in the making, almost another lake. With the low room continuing ahead, I tied off the end of the line and returned to the entrance, an hour and a half after beginning the search. I felt well rewarded.

In the A-frame, Lucy's meter analysed the water from the cave. Only the top six metres could be called truly fresh. Below that the salinity increased gradually with a sudden sharp rise at the shimmering layer. There the brackish water suddenly became as saline as the sea. To all intents and purposes we had found our freshwater lens.

It had been obvious while swimming along the halocline that the cave life favoured the lower layer. In the tannic layer above, only detritivores swam, feeding in the rich organic water before moving back into the cooler salt-water below. It was there that the predators, *Lucifuga* and *Remipedia*, hunted. Sarah dragged a plankton net through the new cave and a new creature emerged, a Cirolanid isopod. Among the largest of the little cave crustaceans, this creature looked something like a small, aquatic wood-louse. It was probably a bottom-dweller, scavenging in the sediments, but the specimens that we caught were swimming free in the clear water below the halocline.

Later dives in Asgard, the new cave, revealed another, deeper chamber. Across the aston hall the cave dropped steeply into a breakdown choke on the far side. To the left of the choke, a well-decorated chamber in the saltwater layer had the purest formations, but all ways on were blind. Asgard was an enigma, a peculiar cave that seemed to be entirely enclosed within the rock. There was no definite outlet, other than micro-fissures in the rock. Although it contained the most populous cave-fauna so far encountered, there were no serpulid worms, no shrimps, no sponges. Apart from the errant moray in the entrance, the only life in the cave was of a type which, over millennia, had completely adapted to an existence in total, enclosed darkness.

The other entrance in the smaller nearby lake was explored by Rob Parker. It led into a sister cave to Asgard,

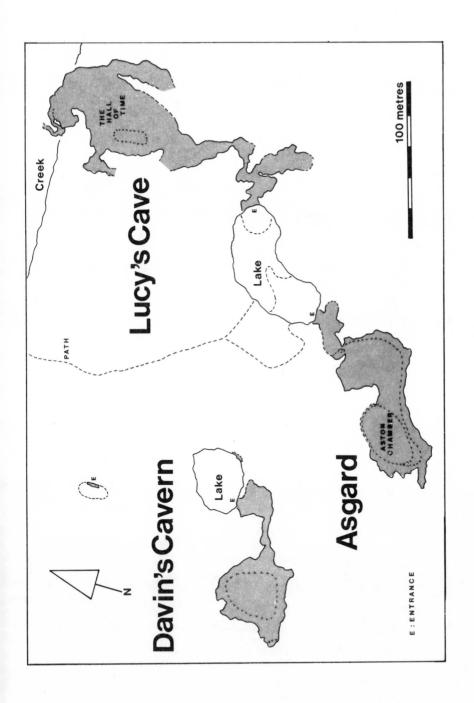

N

Davin's Cavern

Lucy's Cave

THE
HALL
OF
TIME

Creek

PATH

Lake

Asgard

Lake

ASTON
CHAMBER

E : ENTRANCE

100 metres

Davin's Cavern, named phonetically after our young mascot from Sweeting's Cay. Like Asgard, it appeared to be an enclosed, solutional cavern, heavily populated with both cave crustaceans and speleothems, and neatly bisected by a halocline.

As the start of a long-term project to discover whether the halocline was having a second formational effect on the caves, Lucy asked us to place small bags in the caves at different points and different depths. Each of these bags contained a piece of Bahamian limestone and a fragment of marble. Each had been weighed previously in Britain, to six decimal places of a gram. We were going to leave these tablets in the caves for several years. Such precise measurement would reveal whether the caves were still being actively dissolved at any level; by comparing the weights of the limestone and marble (which have known rates of dissolution), scientists might be able to discover how quickly any such activity is taking place.

66 Devon and Aunt Natasha

67 (*left*) Leo Dickinson prepares his parachute in the A-frame

68 (*right*) Peter Scoones filming *Remipedia* in the A-frame

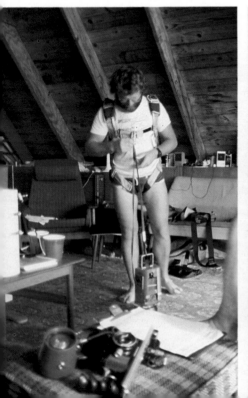

69 (*left*) Manta Hole from above, with the Zodiac inflatable in place for the skydive

70 (*below*) Leo Dickinson splashes down with precise accuracy into Manta Hole

71 (*opposite*) Lucy Heath and the dancing fish in Lothlorien

72 (*left*) Rob Parker struggles through the mangroves and thorn scrub to Asgard

73 (*right*) Rob Palmer and Rob Parker at the Asgard entrance, on the first exploration dive

74 The shallow, three metre deep 'aston' chamber in Asgard appears to be held up only by the massive column in the centre

11

Along the Great North Road

In the northern corner of Big Creek was a group of blue holes with currents that were much stronger than those further down the bay. Rob and Julian, on a break from the filming, chose the two most promising entrances and went to explore.

They picked their time carefully. At full inflow, whirl-pools appeared at the mouths of the caves; the currents here were not the gentle flow of the inland holes but an underground tidal race! As the inflow slackened, the two entered the water and moved tentatively into their selected caves. They disappeared almost simultaneously.

For those on the surface, the filming over, the wait was interminable. Time passed slowly until, at last, Rob's head broke the surface. Within moments Julian was out too, staggering through the shallows to the boat, where he could de-kit. His reel was empty, and we eagerly asked him how it went.

'Well,' he said, pulling at the straps, 'it reminded me of Helm's Deep last year, when I looked down that big shaft and thought "this is like parachuting", and I sat on that little ledge, adjusted my buoyancy, got everything perfect, and then launched myself off. This was exactly the same situation – Helm's Deep Two! I got pretty nervous about the distance and the depth, though. It all seemed far too easy.

'It was all one big rift – I couldn't see the bottom but the walls were at least ten metres apart and I kept meeting huge boulders that were jammed across it. I tended to dodge under those. I don't know whether that was a good idea but it seemed to be the way the cave was going. I swam deeper and deeper, and hit forty-two metres at one point. Then I rose back up a sand slope – which might have been the floor – and my line ran out just as I hit my "thirds".

'Anyway, I swam back along this huge tunnel, feeling pretty chuffed – 150 metres of line straight into a big, deep cave!'

The cave that Rob had explored had been more constricted. He had gone down into a forty-five degree rift, less than half a metre wide, strewn with jammed boulders. Belaying the line where he could, he had wormed his way in and out of the choke until suddenly he emerged in the roof of a large passage. Deflating his jacket, he cruised down through the void until Julian's line suddenly swam into view, out of the gloom. Rather than follow it (not knowing where it led and being close to his air limit), he had returned along the narrow cleft he had gone in.

The huge cave ran almost due north beneath the island, away from the bay. Because it was such an obvious underwater highway, a main water-carrying passage, they nicknamed it Great North Road. The name stuck.

Inland, almost directly in line and less than a kilometre away from the marine cave, were two lakes, each with a blue hole. When the marine cave inflowed, those in the lakes boiled. When the currents reversed, the opposite happened. It looked as though a link was likely and this might provide some of the answers to the tidal hydrology of the holes. What was more, it would provide some exciting and extremely demanding cave-diving!

To ease their problems underground, Julian and Rob made an overland survey from creek to lake. With this, they would be able to chart their progress on subsequent dives, overlaying the surface and underground surveys to see how close they were getting to the lake. It also gave them some idea of which direction to take underwater: if faced with a choice of passages in the cave, they would be aware of which compass bearing was likely to lead them towards the blue hole in the lake.

They made the decision to dive together along the Great North Road, both because the cave was large enough and clear enough to justify it, and because of the extra psychological reassurance that company gives. The exploration was going to be long and deep. Narcosis was a major concern, always more ready to strike at a solo diver, whose mind would be on edge as soon as the dive started.

Even so, if anything were to go wrong far in and deep down, there would be little the other diver could do about it. Such circumstances could lead to complete disaster. They made a conscious decision to leap-frog each other, diving a few minutes apart, with Rob taking over exploration when Julian left off. They would be close enough to help each other out of certain predicaments, but far enough apart so that the panic of an extreme crisis would not kill both. The plan also allowed each diver more room to work, to make decisions without thinking for a second person, and yet still have the psychological reassurance of knowing he was not entirely alone.

To make the dive, they would wear an additional 94-cubic foot tank on their backs, as well as the usual side-mounted 80s. Because air must be breathed at the pressure of the surrounding water, tanks that might last over an hour at the surface would provide only ten or fifteen minutes of air. At forty metres, the surrounding pressure is five times greater than that on the land above.

The inflowing current was used as an aid, carrying Julian into the cave, conserving air for more urgent use deeper inside the system. He came to the end of his previous line, tied the new reel on and moved into unknown country.

Within fifteen metres, he entered an area of rockfall, a chaos of boulders jammed across the rift, obscuring the way on. The current swept frustratingly through cracks too small for man into the continuing cave beyond. He squeezed cautiously into the maze, easing his way between the perched blocks. His progress was slowly channelled down towards a narrow slot. There were two ways through. He tried the left-hand one but his back-mounted tank caught on the rock: his shape was wrong and he would not fit through. He could peer between the rocks into open cave on the other side; this was the final pinch of the choke. He went right, into an angled rift, half a metre wide. Again, with the bulky back-mount, he was defeated.

At a depth of thirty-six metres, he was growing concerned about the amount of air he was wasting. At that depth air flows fast. He came to a decision. His back-pack, used on the way in, had long ago reached its 'third'. He pulled off the straps and wriggled free of the encumbering tank. Leaving it on a stable rock by the side of the line, he passed through the constriction with only his side-mounts.

Fifty metres on, the cave narrowed again. By now Julian was reaching the limits of his air supply. The line was cut from the reel and tied to the cave wall, and he turned round to see Rob's lights gleaming in the darkness behind.

Rob had arrived at the first choke and, seeing the back-pack, had immediately realised what Julian had done. Instead of following Julian's example, he had scouted the choke further. A few metres lower down there was a hole in the boulders, just large enough to negotiate with the bulky back-mounted tank. With his full complement of air, he continued down the newly-explored cave to meet Julian.

They manoeuvred past each other with a brief wave. Julian, low on air, headed out, while Rob tied his own reel to the end of Julian's line. The next constriction was easily passed, but beyond it, the cave suddenly plunged deeper, forcing Rob to a depth of sixty metres. This was the lowest depth on the decompression tables that he carried, he could risk going no deeper.

Below him the rift dropped vertically into unknown

depths but the roof lay at precisely sixty metres for as far as he could see. He scraped along the ceiling, his eyes fixed on this depth gauge, until the roof rose again. Breathing more easily he kept in the shallower passage, reaching the limit of his air supply as another boulder pile came into view. Belaying the line, he looked into several constrictions, high in the passage. None was large enough to negotiate with three tanks on. The way on must lie deeper in the rift and would have to wait for another day.

Passing the deep section on the way back, he noticed that his lamp battery, housed in a circular tube, had been squeezed into a triangular prism shape by the pressure of the water – a salutary reminder of the effects of depth.

It was a relief to return to the large entrance passage and join Julian in decompression before surfacing. No sooner were they out, than they were working on a new plan of attack. Rob's discovery of the alternative route through the first choke enabled them to carry more air deeper into the cave, using stage tanks to increase their range from the surface. Another dive from the Big Creek entrance would involve the divers in original exploration well below sixty metres, over 200 metres into the cave. Working under pressure at that depth while breathing ordinary compressed air made that option an exceedingly dangerous one to take.

Instead, they decided to approach the system from the inland lake. Hauling gear across the broken limestone and slippery mangrove flats between sea and lake, Julian struggled down into the inland hole that lay closest to the Great North Road.

A strong current was bowing out, making progress difficult but ensuring that the view in front was always clear. By the time he had forced his way to a depth of twenty-two metres, seventy-five metres in, it was obvious that the cave was not what they had hoped for. It was far too small and constricted to be the main exit for the water from the huge marine system. The flow emerged from a boulder ruckle at the far end of the cave and, despite vigorous excavation, there proved to be no way through. This cave seemed only to be a feeder system in a much bigger, deeper complex, an exploratory red herring.

It seemed to us that the Great North Road might be more than the straightforward cave we had originally thought, and might reach far beyond the blue holes in the lakes. On the map, the next possible stop beyond the lakes was the massive blue hole complex at the end of Lightbourn Cay Creek, where the channel dissolved into a series of curving entrances, a massive aston collapse at the end of the tidal creek.

As with Zodiac Creek and Aquarius, it appeared that the much larger Lightbourn Creek had come to a premature end at an underground cave entrance. The creek wound its way in from the eastern shore of Grand Bahama, like so many others that paralleled it to north and south. Unlike those, which bisected the island, Lightbourn Cay Creek stopped short of the western shore. Perhaps this was a surface illusion? It now looked as though the creek did in fact continue, but underground. The tidal flow which disgorged from the Great North Road and its companion caves was that which disappeared into the caves of Lightbourn Creek.

Unfortunately these entrances were too remote for us to explore on this expedition. Accessible only for a brief period at high tide, the approach even then was long and circuitous. Just to reach the entrances was quite an undertaking in itself. With our limited resources we could not afford the loss of time that such a diversion would take. We abandoned the idea of approaching the system from the inland lake.

There was nothing for it but to make one final push from the sea, a push that looked as though it might be limited by depth rather than distance into the cave.

The depth limit for the dive was set at seventy-five metres, the limit of the gauges the divers wore. This would make it, as far as we knew, the deepest underground dive ever attempted by British cave-divers using compressed

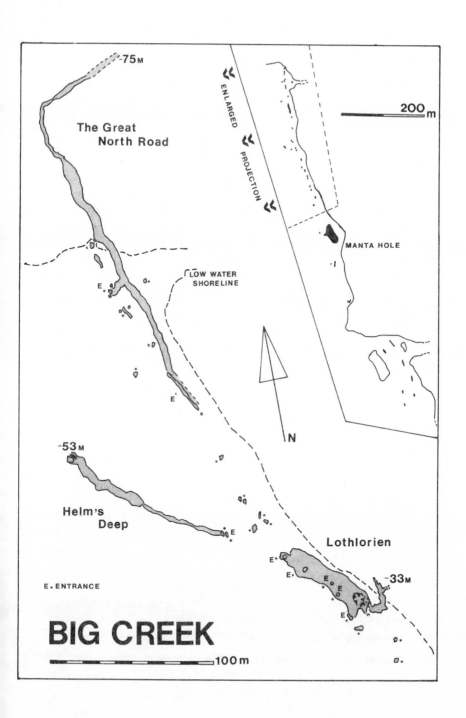

-75M

The Great
North Road

ENLARGED

PROJECTION

MANTA HOLE

LOW WATER
SHORELINE

200 m

N

-53M

Helm's
Deep

E

Lothlorien

-33M

E. ENTRANCE

BIG CREEK

100 m

air. If they succeeded, if the cave went that deep, they would be over 200 metres inside and still in the main water flow. The possible decompression profiles for such a dive were consulted. We were using the U.S. Navy's Exceptional Exposure tables now. If something went wrong, the first stop could be as deep as twenty-seven metres. Julian decided to place spare tanks for decompression there. Each diver would, in addition, be carrying four tanks apiece, with a hand-held 80 in addition to the three tanks worn on the earlier attempt. Every tank would have its own regulator, and the staging unit, once used, would be left by the line at the first constriction. From there, the divers would continue wearing three full tanks each.

The complete dive, there and back, and including decompression, was likely to take three or four hours, and the long immersion in cool water could significantly lower body temperature. Warmth was essential so both divers donned an extra layer of neoprene, a vest and hood that we had brought for just such a purpose. This might be the Bahamas but the deep cave temperature was colder by several degrees than the warm surface seas. The compressor would be taken along in the boat in case extra air was needed in an emergency. Sarah and I would remain on the surface, ready to provide support if necessary.

As Rob and Julian stripped and checked their equipment the night before, Leo asked out of curiosity whether they ever became emotional before such a dive. Julian replied quietly that he tried to ignore emotional responses and stay as matter of fact as he could. Getting over-emotional simply detracted from the job in hand and he had no intention of coming to a sticky end through over-imagination. Rob added that at times like these control was essential; dealing with events such as regulators jamming open, or line entanglements, were more immediately important than trying to imagine more exotic mishaps.

'I try to get little sensors going in the back of my head,' he said, 'telling me exactly what to do. If I'm starting to breathe a little bit heavily, they tell me to slow down and ease off. You've got to be a machine!'

They set off into the cave within a minute of each other, at 11.30 the next morning. With their array of tanks, they were on their way down the enormous rift passage, deep under the island.

The staging tanks, breathed to their inward limit, were tied on the line by the first choke. Beyond the sixty metre deep abyss, Rob unclipped his new reel, and fastened it to the end of the old line. He had attached a 250-watt headpiece to his battery unit and now he turned it on. The cave suddenly seemed as bright as day and he could clearly see the route ahead, down below him through a further narrowing of the cave.

Moving cautiously, Rob followed the still-descending passage, checking the walls as he passed for any flakes or crevices in which the line could catch and hinder his return. Another restriction loomed ahead. His gauge read seventy metres. He passed through the new stricture, the walls tight on either side. Julian, above Rob, hung back at the first constriction, encumbered by Leo's Photosonic housing. He paused to tie it to the line, intending to recover it on the way out. As he did so, Rob, several metres below, hit thirds on his second tank. Adjusting his buoyancy, and getting his trim right, he changed regulators smoothly, moving on to the last of his three tanks. He was almost at the maximum planned depth of seventy-five metres and still going down.

Then the unforeseen happened. To change his regulators he had been obliged to let go of the 250-watt torch in his hand. Floating beside him in the water, it had slipped through a loose coil of line and become entangled. Rob recovered the torch and attempted to untangle the knot. At seventy-five metres, narcosis was having a subtle effect on his brain. His first attempt simply made matters worse. As he tugged at a loose loop, the torch swung round and he was blinded by the intense beam. His bubbles disturbed fine silt from the walls and roof of the constriction and visibility dropped to under a metre. Deep underground, in a narrow crevice over a fathomless void, he was rapidly getting into the same sort of situation that had killed Frank Martz in Benjamin's Blue Hole, more than ten years before.

Rob's sensors told him there was only one thing to do — take his knife to the job!

Making absolutely sure that he had a firm grip on the side of the tangle that led out of the cave, he managed to get his knife from its sheath and cut the light free. The line reel slipped from his fingers, tumbling down out of sight into the darkness below, to depths that might be well in excess of 100 metres. He backed out through the narrow passage, joining Julian in clearer water at the higher constriction. Fully in control again, they turned and made their way back along the dark, twisting corridors, through the jumbled breakdown piles, to the open cave and their first decompression stop.

If the entanglement had happened at twenty metres then, despite the lack of visibility, Rob could have happily taken time to solve it. In zero visibility, seventy-five metres down in a shaft that plunged much deeper, he had neither air nor time to spare. Matters could only have got worse; his decision had been the only right one to make. He was breathing air deeper than he or any other British cave-diver had done before, and was risking quite enough.

The drama had taken barely forty minutes. Back beneath the entrance, establishing themselves on a ledge deep in the huge passage, Rob and Julian began a three hour wait. Their first decompression stop was in total darkness, out of sight of the cave mouth, twenty metres down. They moved up in three metre stages, edging the resident lobster population off ledge after ledge, each stop taking longer than the last as the nitrogen slowly de-gassed from their body tissues. As they rose closer to the surface and into the daylight zone Leo slipped down to join them and shoot some film. He was amazed to see Rob wedged firmly on a ledge and dropping off to sleep!

Four hours after the dive began the two divers broke surface, parched with thirst from the continual trickle of saltwater past their mouthpieces, and with wrinkled and shivering skin.

The Great North Road had been explored for 270 metres, to a final but by no means terminal depth of seventy-five metres. It was no ordinary cave, the passages paid little heed to former sea-levels. It was a gigantic, open chasm, a massive fracture of the rock that had split apart in the far past, when the island had stood as a plateau high above the waves. No true floor had been seen by the divers: the stretch that seemed so had turned out – as the divers had discovered by swimming underneath it – to be banks of sand piled on top of collapsed blocks. Julian felt that the last fifty metres had been one enormous boulder choke, below which the cave fell away to unpredictable depths. A descent to the base could be limited by technology rather than nature for some time yet.

Later that evening, as Leo poured each of them a celebratory Bacardi and Coke, he turned to Julian and said, 'How do you follow that?'

'Not yet,' said Julian emphatically. He paused and tipped a generous amount of the drink down his throat. He looked at the glass reflectively.

'I suppose the real challenge would be to join it to Lightbourn Cay. Of course, it won't be done by us, but maybe we've started a bit of work that might be finished off in a decade . . . or half a century!'

Rob, smiling, added his thoughts, 'It could be that one day divers will start their decompression where we turned round – their first stop could be at seventy-five metres.'

'It's a major system,' said Julian, emptying his glass and looking hopefully at the bottle in Leo's hand. 'Certainly as divers improve and technology advances the place we've been today will seem nothing – it'll be just the beginning of a very spectacular through-trip!'

12

The Halls of Time

Tuesday lunchtime, 24 July. The A-frame is in its usual
state, with gear strewn everywhere from the morning's
filming. Sarah and Rob are cleaning regulators, ready for
an afternoon in Sagittarius. I am wiping the sealing rings
on my underwater camera and reloading film for a dive in
Davin's Cavern. Rob has spent the morning there, tying up
loose ends.

'Strange how the formations there are so different from
those in Asgard – more 'mites and 'tites than columns –
well worth seeing.'

'Anything left to push?'

'I don't think so. I've looked in the most likely places.
The pit at the end just walls out in little holes, and I kept
coming back on the line when I checked out the walls.'

So that afternoon my dive would be only for recording:
taking what photographs I could in the brown water,
catching animals and collecting water samples for Lucy.
She was already there, having gone up-creek that morning
with Rob to sit out a full tidal cycle. He had left her there
with her Walkman, Tolkien's *Lord of the Rings* and a
day's worth of bug repellent, measuring how much the
water in the lakes was rising and falling with the tides.
Though the vertical range in the nearby creek was almost a
metre, it seemed to be less than half that in the lakes,

which were only about two hundred metres away. Six hours spent out in the bush, measuring water levels, was dedication indeed!

The ride up the creek in the whaler was quick. The tide was rising and the channel was clearly visible. The zig-zag route was becoming like a well-remembered country road at home. Once we could anticipate the turns it became so much easier. By chance I arrived as Lucy was testing the tide in the creek. She beamed at me, looking pleased with herself. Music seeped faintly from the headphones of the Walkman as she quickly jotted down her notes and caught the bow-line. Together we splashed my gear through the remaining shallows.

'Where are we going?' she asked.

'Davin's Cavern . . . catch some bugs and get you some water.'

'Don't you want to dive in my new cave?' she said innocently.

'Eh?'

'I've found a new cave . . . just across the lake from Asgard. And much bigger.'

This news was received with mixed emotions. It went without saying that I would prefer to look somewhere new but as Rob had finished the exploration of Davin's Cavern I had not bothered to reload my line reel. All I had was fifty metres or so of line and if the cave went anywhere that would not get me very far. Lucy looked at the almost empty reel.

'It's a really big entrance,' she said accusingly.

We ended up on the Asgard track, Lucy humming to herself in that irritating way people wearing headphones do. It was a hot day and sweat soon began to run down my face. The new entrance lay at the eastern end of the lake. The only way to it was through the lake itself, at this point more mangrove swamp than open water. Our ankles sank into mud, and the sulphurous smell of disturbed rotting vegetation crept into our nostrils. Gear snagged on sprawling branches and aerial roots. Dragonflies soared over the low greenery, bright red and sharp, electric blue, dipping into the flowering bromeliads. A small patch of solid rock was the sign to drop our gear.

The entrance was certainly big. Overhung by shrubbery at the far end of the pool, it lay beneath the flat, spreading branches of a bright green thorn. An air of quiescence surrounded the lake. With only the two of us there, and just one of us diving alone, there was none of the usual noise and anticipatory chatter of a group. Lucy waited while I pieced my equipment together and then waded out across the lake with me. I peered down through the tannic liquid into the entrance. Tall, wheat-like grasses grew below the surface, fringing the mouth of the cave. Lucy looked in with my main light in her hand, but could see nothing.

'It looks deep,' she said, suddenly serious.

A solid root grew from the rock, an ideal tie-off spot for the line. I ran the usual gear checks, turned on my lights and slipped underwater.

It *is* deep. As my eyes adjust, I can see it stretching away on either side, in sunlight that filters with an eerie tint through the brown hue. Huge rocks litter the floor and a fine slope of organic debris – branches, leaves and silt – leads down into the darkness.

Within a few metres the cave begins to cheat. The passage constricts. I am being over-ambitious, with camera, line reel and collection bottles in my hands, and I am clumsy. I stir up more silt than I ought. The cave gets smaller and demands I make a choice. The way on is very low, only a few centimetres of clear water above the mung. On the right, it seems a little larger and a few brown stalagmites are dimly visible. I move that way, taking a water sample as I go.

The cave at this level is not impressive. Trying to negotiate a narrow corridor, my tanks scrape flowstone on either side. The roof is just high enough to allow me to tilt my head back and look ahead. What I see is not encouraging, and I feel a small surge of claustrophobia. I stop moving and try to sort out the equipment. My brown wake catches me up and I hang there for a minute or two, breathing carefully, until it settles. Enticingly, by my left shoulder, a tiny hole looks out into a larger room and clearer water. But this narrow, constricted passage is not the key.

Squirming backwards, I hope that my tanks are not going to catch in crevices or on columns. There is no room to turn and sort such a problem out; I can't even move my hands to my sides with all the gear they hold. I can just about manage to reel in the line as I go, holding it at arm's length in front, keeping it taut to avoid a tangle behind me that could prove disastrous. I might as well be doing it with my eyes shut with this mung rising round me like a blizzard. This is not a nice situation to have got into.

A long time later, I push back into a bigger cave. I pause for a moment to slow my breathing and to watch the storm abate. I recall a little globe I had as a child which, when shaken, raised tiny white flakes in an artificial snowstorm. The flakes settled quickly to reveal the winter scene, the flurry dying down in exactly the same way as the whirling mung in front of me returns the cave water to a reasonable clarity within a few moments.

The way through into the half-seen chamber must lie through the first low section. Now that the blizzard has died down, it looks as if I must play snow-plough. I swim at the gap, pushing a bow-wave of mung ahead and moving fast to stay in clear water. Pause and belay the line at the squeeze, to show me the way back through the constriction. I have no wish to sandwich myself between floor and roof on the way out.

Beyond the low, mung-filled squeeze lies another, of solid rock. Again, a careful belay, and a cautious contortion into the chamber I had seen from above. Fine, here I am in a big, clear cave, below the halocline, but with a certain uneasiness about my return to daylight. The way in was very difficult compared to other caves. Off on my right, the cave is a forest of white columns; in front of my eyes, a myriad of tiny creatures move in the water, but I am lured on by the beckoning void ahead. The reel runs faster as the remainder of my line races out. I follow the cave until a small tug in my hand brings me to a halt. I am at the end of the line, and of the cave also. Ahead, a blank wall stretches across my path. I pendulum from side to side in a wide half-circle, in an effort to see a way on. A white brotulid, shrinking from the pressure waves, slides into a handy crack. My depth gauge reads twenty-four metres. Perhaps I have come too deep? I tie the end of the line to a flake.

Peering into the darkness beyond the pillars, I have a strange premonition, a peculiar and distinct feeling that I am very close to something big. The cave has an atmosphere of its own, different to the others. It *definitely* holds a secret.

The return through the rock squeeze is horrific, worse than I imagined it could be. Every hose, every wire, every piece of equipment that could possibly get caught or stuck does so. Whether it is my sense of disappointment and frustration that affects my co-ordination, or simply the lack of visibility and awkward shape of the constriction, it takes me several minutes to get everything through. Going down was tricky, coming the other way is an uphill struggle. Near the end, I think seriously about de-kitting underwater, but suddenly, fortunately everything slips through. The mung is an anti-climax. Though my air-bubbles had disturbed it as I struggled in between the rocks, I can still see the trail I gouged out on my descent. Head down, I gouge back again.

The brief statutory wait below the surface is a relief, a chance to rest. Black holes lie behind the boulders at the far side of the entrance. Perhaps they are the key to the cave? I finish the film on reflections, on algae, on tiny mosquito fish dancing between the mangrove roots. The dive has been a peculiar experience, a juxtaposition of extremes. I feel as though the cave has been playing with me.

75 Big Creek and Lightbourn Creek, looking north-east. In the foreground on the left are the entrances to the Great North Road system; behind these is the lake with the small blue hole; and in the far distance the winding channel of Lightbourn Creek comes to a premature end when its waters go underground to the sea

76 Constricted underwater cave

77 (*left*) Julian Walker in front of the entrance to the Great North Road, looking at the whirlpool during the fierce inflow

78 (*below*) Silhouetted in the cave mouth, Rob Parker checks the passing of the hours while Julian Walker dozes

79 (*opposite right*) Lucy Heath at the entrance to Lucy's Cave

80 (*opposite below*) Air bubbles stream to the roof as Rob Parker passes a tall group of formations in Lucy's Cave, in the entrance passages to the Hall of Time

81 Rob Parker swims along the wall of the beautifully decorated Hall of Time in Lucy's Cave

82 A peculiar formation in the Hall of Time: a stalagmite which has collapsed and regrown

It fell to Rob Parker to reveal the secret of Lucy's Cave a few days later. While Sarah and I were trawling for cave-life in Asgard and placing Lucy's bags of limestone down the aston slope at the far end of the cave, Rob ploughed alone through the deep banks of sediment that filled the left-hand wall of Lucy's Cave, on the faint suspicion that there might be a larger cavern on the other side.

He was gone for almost two hours. When I surfaced from Asgard, after depositing the final bags of limestone for Lucy, the two girls were growing concerned at his non-return. By now his air would be extremely low and they were afraid that he might have got into difficulties somewhere underwater in the cave. Still fully-kitted, I struggled across the shallow lake to the other entrance.

I found Rob safely decompressing underwater, looking as happy as he could be. He raised three fingers, and pointed to the surface. His waiting time was nearly up. As we broke surface he pulled his mask off and grinned, losing his customary cool.

'Rob,' he gasped, 'you just would not believe how big it gets down there.'

Through the drift of mung, the passage had suddenly enlarged. Swimming along a clear tunnel, below the halocline, he realised that he had lost sight of the walls but swam on in the darkness for almost 200 metres before they re-appeared. In this leviathan chamber, stalagmites grew on stalagmites, the older formations leaning at a crazy angle to their later regrowth.

There was little time left to us for more exploration. Despite the length of his first dive, and the additional decompression penalty involved because of it, Rob and I returned that evening in a final attempt to uncover the secret of Lucy's Cave.

So often this happens: the finest discoveries come at the end of an expedition, the final, tantalising prize which drives home to you how little you really know, and how much there is left to explore. By a strange trick of fate, our exploration of the caves below Sweeting's Cay had followed a progression of increasing splendour and scientific complexity. Aquarius, Scorpio and Gemini, the first to be explored, had been one step beyond the marine caves that lay offshore. Virgo and Sagittarius had revealed to us untainted crystal halls in 1983, and a profusion of life in 1984. Pisces had produced *Remipedia*, almost on cue, and its shallow aston chambers which provided the clues to the story of the cavern's past development. Then had come the lens caves – Asgard and Davin's Cavern – the most cryptic cave-environments of all. The entire process had followed a curiously logical sequence, as though some force had been guiding us along a pre-ordained path. In this weird progression, Lucy's Cave came like a final reward.

We dived at 6 p.m. precisely, Rob waving me ahead. He knew the geography of the new squeeze better than I did and was giving me the benefit of clearer visibility. I followed the thin cord down the slope to a line junction and swung left along the new route. As I ploughed into the morass, I realised the dedication of his earlier exploration. Even though my helmet scraped the ceiling, my mask and mouthpiece were buried deep in the organic mousse. I swam blindly, my fingers tracing the thin line that was my only link with reality. The camera unit was an encumbrance, and I was more than usually aware of the countless tons of rock above my head.

As abruptly as it began, it ended. We emerged, one after the other, in a clear passage below the halocline. The line snaked off into the distance, rounding a bend several metres further on. Rob took the lead now, while I worked the camera, photographing his progress down the cave.

The passage grew. Until my eyes re-adjusted, all I could see was Rob's silhouette, ten or fifteen metres ahead, and stalagmites that faded into the distance on either side of his torch beam. I was unprepared for this. I had thought Pisces large but here we were swimming into the biggest underwater chamber I had ever seen. I turned out all but one of my lights and dropped further behind, trying to gain from his torches some reference for this colossal cave. His lights picked out, faintly, the roof above and a broken floor below, but they faded into nothing on either side. At length he paused by a single pillar which grew near the end of the line, a crooked form whose tip was angled to the stalagmite below. It beckoned us into the unexplored beyond.

There was an awesome aura of age about the place. Huge columns lay sprawled in ruin across the floor, fragmented by some cataclysmic collapse in the far distant past, scattered like the ruins of a pagan temple that had been cast down by an angry and implacable god.

We followed a gigantic wall of rock which had toppled to one side, stalagmite pillars bristling in crooked confusion amidst vertical columns of regrowth. Perspective swam, and I found difficulty in orientating my vision. In the open darkness I experienced a slight attack of vertigo as I hung in the centre of the room, out of sight of either wall, and with the roof sloping at a different angle to the crumpled floor. There was nothing to say which way was truly up, or down, no clear point of reference, until one focused clearly on regrowth, on the last unaltered pillars of time.

As always in our deepest caves, the waters swarmed with life. Blind fish swam freely with little to impede them in the vastness of the cavern. Our lights reflected from a thousand tiny forms in this underwater metropolis, this crowded crustacean city.

I followed Rob in a frenzy of excitement as we searched the perimeters of this enormous cavern, following the walls in convoluted loops, searching alcoves and blind passages. Time and time again, we saw our original line in the distance. Each time but one, we made a circle, and Rob would survey back along the line, to set off again at a different angle, searching for a continuation to the cave. Each run out provided a new question which we knew would probably remain unanswered for years to come.

Along the deepest walls, almost thirty metres down,

were large scallopings in the rock, shapes that indicated a strong current flow in a previous age. These walls were original, unmarked by breakdown, some of the earliest evidence of the cave's formation. On certain columns, at a particular level, were curious bands of brighter crystal. Was there once an ancient freshwater lake whose tidal fluctuation had created this thin band of clean, washed calcite? Was the sharp scalloping evidence that the great cave once carried flowing waters beneath the island, draining through still-undiscovered passages to a reduced Pleistocene sea? Were the shattered formations – the crazy angles, the clean regrowth – the remains of a particular upheaval in the distant island past? Had there been a rise in sea-level between collapse and regrowth that could be accurately dated by examining the crystal cores of the speleothems? All the unnumbered pages of blue hole history unfolded before us as we swam around this monolithic hall of time.

We spent more than an hour exploring the immense cavern before our air ran low. Finally we came to a passage which seemed to continue. While I hung by the line, Rob swam into it as far as he could without losing sight of my lights . . . we had no spare line of our own left now, or time to use it even if we had. It would be courting a foolhardy death to go further. Leaving the enigmatic, virgin passage, we swam reluctantly back along the line, high on the adrenalin rush of discovery, through the low barrier of silt to a long decompression in the gathering dusk.

The high tide of a full moon covered the thorn bush above the entrance as we surfaced in the final flush of sunset. We staggered wearily, without de-kitting, along the forest path to the boat. I felt fulfilled. Despite the scraps of time remaining, the adventure was finished, complete. There could be nothing better, nothing more. For a while, our part in the story of the blue holes was over.

Epilogue

There is a certain dilemma about writing a book like this. On the one hand, there is the onus on us to share our discoveries, to add a small piece to the sum knowledge of mankind.

On the other, there is the very real fear that telling the story, revealing the presence of caves such as these, is the beginning of their end: that the basic, inherent, unforgivable greed and stupidity of a certain part of mankind will rush forward in all its vanity and treat the caves as another plaything to be exploited. Perhaps I am too pessimistic. But if we play with the caves, if we treat them as toys, they will die. They may take some of their despoilers with them, for they will never be an environment that suffers fools. For millions of years life has been adapting beneath the Bahamas, and in other secret places in the world, to exist in such fragile environments. The most unnecessary addition is man.

Those who enter these caves must first learn how to do it without hurting them. They must learn to move without clumsiness, they must learn how and why life exists there, and they must respect their rules. Above all, they must learn about *themselves*, so that both they and the caves will survive if something begins to go wrong. Bravado kills.

Epilogue

It will be many years before the story of blue holes exploration is over; there are longer, deeper and perhaps more magnificent caves still to discover. It might be as well, however, to leave some places entirely alone, so that the future of this delicate, fascinating environment is assured.

Rob Palmer
Bristol 1984

Acknowledgments

We are extremely grateful to HRH the Duke of Kent for Royal Patronage of the 1981–4 British Blue Holes Expeditions. The Zodiac Project was the final result of a tremendous amount of work by many people behind the scenes in addition to those who feature in this book. To all those unsung heroes, companies and individuals, we give our heartfelt thanks:

The Royal Geographical
  Society
The Ghar Parau
  Foundation
Rolex U.K. Ltd
Arrow Air
Moonbridge Shippers Ltd
Zodiac U.K. Ltd
Typhoon Ltd
Wemlor Marine Ltd
Outboard Services
  (Freeport)
3M (U.K.) Thinsulate
  Division
Troll Equipment Ltd
Kodak U.K. Ltd
Dive Care Systems
Bahamas National Trust
Bahamas Ministry of
  Education
Honda U.K. Ltd
C.P.L. Bristol Ltd

Cornwall Mining Services
The Sports Council
Wookey Hole Caves Ltd
Grand Bahama
  Development Co.
Pan American Airways
Freeport Harbour
  Authority
Spirotechnique U.K.
GUL Wetsuits Ltd
The Diving Locker
James Pearsall Ltd
Phoenix Mountaineering
  Ltd
Apeks Marine Ltd
Fuji U.K. Ltd
Varta U.K. Ltd
Grand Bahama Rotary Clubs
Princess Hotels Ltd
SOS Diving Eqpt Ltd
Solomon Bros Ltd
Sea and Sea Ltd

Acknowledgments

John Hinchliffe, Dennis Williams, Jill Yager, John Schlanbusch, John and Mary Brooks, Colin Rose, Martin Gaucci, Doug Silvera, Mike Guy, Jack Rogers, Nick van Beurden, David and Michael Pincus, Godfrey Waugh, Susan Holowesko, Jack Worsfold, Theo and Alex Galanopoulos, Ben Russell, Frank McBratney, Tony Boycott, George Warner, Sir John Rawlins, Bernard Parker, Philip Chapman, Oliver Lloyd, Nic Flemming, Dan Plummer, Peter Smart, Dave and Jenny George, and the people of Sweeting's Cay and MacLean's Town.